"*Shepherding the Sea* is about passion and it makes a compelling read. Few individuals develop and sustain a course in life as has Paul Watson. I suggest that Reese Halter is of a similar vein. Earth's ocean's continue to be degraded by the activities of evermore technically-armed *Homo sapiens*, best evidenced by the demise of our mammalian cousins, the whales. Watson and Halter share a passion for nature and an ability to focus solely on its protection. This book tells the story of our oceans against the backdrop of Paul Watson's amazing zeal for direct action to save every whale possible from slaughter by humans. Let the facts of Watson's actions sink in as you read this text. There is hope for the oceans because there are people like Watson and Halter to make the rest of us sit up and think."

— Dr Christopher Weston, Forest Ecology, University of Melbourne

"Dr Reese Halter's book, *Shepherding the Sea*, is an easy-to-read, enlightened presentation of an increasingly disastrous, human-caused crisis in the world's oceans — one that requires our immediate attention because it not only affects the oceans of the world but also every human on Earth, even if the vast majority of the people are unaware of it."

—Chris Maser, Zoologist, co-author of *Life, The Wonder of it All*

"Few have the passion for, and understanding of, the ecology of the Animal Kingdom to match that of Dr Reese Halter. Over the years, I've had the pleasure of interviewing him on a variety of issues on animals and their survival. What I take away from each interview is Dr Reese's enthusiasm for sharing his knowledge with everyone. After reading *Shepherding the*

Sea, I have a new found appreciation for these magnificent creatures, which make up our planet's sea life. I hope you will be equally inspired to protect them every way we can.

—Alex Witt, Anchor, MSNBC

"If a loved one was on life support, you would do nothing to tamper with it. Yet every single day, we as a species, pollute, overfish and acidify our life support, our oceans.

To future generations that may say, "If they only knew what they were doing," I say this, we did know, we knew that we were breaking the most important and irrefutable Laws of Ecology with absolutely no respect for our kids and their children, we knew we were responsible for the complete mass extinction of so many beautiful and wonderful species and we did very little. We rely on every other species on this planet for our very survival, we need them, they don't need us. If we want to put humanity first, we do this by simply putting us last, put the environment first and you are putting humanity and future generations first. The human race is at war with mother nature, at war with our kids that have not even been born yet. Paul Watson and Reese Halter challenge the way we look at and see the world. It is a realization, of respect and love for nature that all humanity must take onboard now and reconnect to before it is too late. I have always had a deep love of the natural world and it astounds me how some of us lose this as we become adults. If you want to reignite your love for nature and learn some beautiful tales to tell your children and friends, through the eyes of two of humanity's greatest ecologists and story tellers, then *Shepherding The Sea* is for you!"

—Jeff Hansen, Managing Director of Sea Shepherd Australia. Campaign leader, Operation Kimberley Miinimbi, Operation Zero Tolerance, Operation Relentless, Operation Icefish

"Few of us realize how dependent our species is on our oceans. In *Shepherding the Sea*, Dr Reese Halter entertainingly helps us to understand why we need to preserve our oceans and what they do for us. While there are a lot of facts in this book, they are presented in a most engaging way. You will find yourself learning much but anxious to read on to learn what can be done."

—Professor Rollin Richmond, President of Humboldt State University

"*Shepherding the Sea* has captured the essence of the crisis in our oceans. It tells the story of amazing organisms that inhabit it, the terrible consequences of man's attempts to exploit it, and the fight to preserve it that has been Paul Watson's life. Dr Reese Halter has shown us that with knowing comes caring and respect for the sea and all the life that inhabits it."

—Robert Teskey, Distinguished Research Professor, Warnell School of Forestry & Natural Resources, University of Georgia

"Paul Watson's courageous career and his lengthy interview segments provide compelling linkage for Dr Reese Halter's cry from the heart, a call to action to save the sea and stop the war against nature. Our oceans are ailing and the fate of the whales, sharks, tunas, sea turtles, krill and albatrosses are documented with sobering detail in *Shepherding the Sea*, making it clear that the time to act is now, if we love this planet. With political action predominantly short term, our hope for change rests with the next generation. Dr Halter's book needs to be required reading for every undergraduate & secondary student, worldwide. With this compelling evidence in hand, they can be the catalyst for change we so desperately need."

—Dr Stephen Johnson, Assistant Head of School at Pickering College

"*Shepherding the Sea* is a brilliant exposé, written with passion and soul, much of it heart-wrenching to read. Most people do not realize that marine life and animals have perceptions, emotions, awareness, and feel pain. They experience life as we do and their lives are as valuable to them as ours are to us. Dr Reese Halter has alerted us that we need worldwide progressive and compassionate legislation to be grounded in science and driven by ethics."

—Professor John Ryan, University of Winnipeg, author of *The Saga of the Three Compañeros – Pantera, Leo and El Tigre*

"This is a story about the sea, a world apart from most humans and not on the radar of most as something that should cause much concern. However, Dr Halter makes the strong case that the health of the sea is intimately connected to the health and future of the human race. He presents the case that over-exploitation of marine resources, climate change and pollution (particularly plastics) are sabotaging marine ecosystems, greatly reducing marine biodiversity and placing human dependence on the sea for resources (food, medicines) at great risk. He backs this up with a formidable and frightening set of statistics that confirm the recent record of our stewardship of the sea is disgraceful.

Dr Halter details the complex web of marine life and the interdependence of species, from plankton and krill through to predators at the top of the food chain. There is a great deal of information here, some of it quite surprising. He provides excellent details of, and threats to, some of the iconic marine species – tuna, turtles, sharks, albatross, dolphins and whales.

The narrative is wound around the life and exploits of Paul Watson, founder of the Sea Shepherd Conservation Society and charts his exploits over 30 years in what was and remains open warfare on the high seas against poachers of marine life at risk and particularly whales. Watson is a controversial character, maligned by those with vested interests, but widely supported by the community at large. His exploits, often risky and dangerous and backed by passionate volunteers and donations from interested parties, have without any doubt greatly assisted in curbing the exploitation of marine species. His life reads like a thriller.

This book by Halter is a very valuable account of the precious nature of our marine ecosystems and the very real risks posed for their future. I thoroughly recommend the book."

—Professor Emeritus Roger Sands, Canterbury University, author of
Forestry in a Global Context

"Dr Reese Halter is a storyteller. He tells stories of bees, of trees, and of countless other parts of our beautiful, majestic natural world and the parts of it that are increasingly corrupted. He does not really tell his own stories but rather the stories of champions of the environment. The goal of most of his past stories seem to hang on the question – what can you do to keep the beautiful and the functional while eliminating the awful and the ugly? The voice he has always used is that of an angry agitated scientist – if you like – a scientist turned advocate. This is sometimes a difficult world to live in because evidence is the fuel for the advocacy but advocacy itself is enriched in subjectivity. In his latest book *Shepherding the Sea*, Halter tells the story of Paul Watson and the Sea Shepherd Conservation Society. Starting with some violent episodes in the 1970s and continuing to the present, the book tries to put the advocacy of Watson into both a scientific and political context. This is a difficult story both to tell and read. Governments world-wide say that environmental policy should be based on scientific evidence, but then the stories are told in the book about how the Japanese whaling fleet uses the hunt for science as a cover for the hunt for cash. Such stories reflect that ultimate human tragedy: we are driven to do things that we know will impose tragedy and hardship on ourselves, now or in the future. We seem to endlessly hope that the planet will repair whatever damage we do it and this hope seems to be achieved by willful blindness to the truth contained in the evidence. The food chains of the seas are shortening, the oceans are becoming acidic, the atmosphere is becoming warmer. All of these things are connected to each other and they drive people like Paul Watson to do something tangible to stop the trends, and people like Reese Halter to widen the public's appreciation for what looks like lawlessness.

The book is easy to read and the message is immediate: if society waits for lawmakers on their own to make environmental policies to fit the evidence, there may be no evidence left to collect. Citizens must first change their own behaviour, then that of their families, then communities, and lastly by these actions force changes to policies at all levels of governance. Halter is doing what he can, Watson has committed his life doing what he can, and the rest is up to the rest of us. This is the story of all of our lives."

—Professor Emeritus Douglas Larson, University of Guelph, author of *Storyteller Guitar*

ISBN 978-0-9817152-4-7

ISBN 0-9817152-4-9

EarthCallingSOS.com

50% of the proceeds from the sale of *Shepherding the Sea*
go to Sea Shepherd Australia

Printed in Canada

March 2017

Shepherding the Sea:
The Race to
Save our Oceans

Dr Reese Halter

Foreword by Dr Bob Brown

FOR RJ —
The Whales
need your help!

#Save Nature Now

Earth Doctor Reese

For my brother and sister: Jason and Diana – with love.

If all the animals were to vanish
mankind would die from a great loneliness of spirit.

—Chief Seattle, Suqwamish and Duwamish

Contents

Acknowledgements

In January 2009, my friend, colleague and mentor, Chris Maser, suggested I write a book on the state of the oceans. After completing books on bees and trees, I undertook the manuscript on seas in March of 2013. I am deeply grateful to my brother Jason Roy for his unstinting love, confidence and warm hospitality during this most exciting adventure. For my childhood classmate, exquisite communicator and friend, Joe Paraskevas, thank you for all your sagacious advice since I began broadcasting in 2003. Gregg Cockrell of MSNBC television, New York City, first booked me for an interview in 2005, thank you for your loyal friendship and believing in my dreams. My dear friend Rich Travis has been a constant source of encouragement, funny stories and steadfast ally since we first joined forces during my early MSNBC broadcasting days. My friend and colleague Jeff Hansen, Managing Director of Sea Shepherd Australia, kindly facilitated my first interview with Captain Paul Watson in June of 2013. Lisa Agabian, Director of Media Relations & Communications, Sea Shepherd USA, and Farrah Smith, Senior Leadership Giving & Development Officer, Sea Shepherd USA, helped arrange my second meeting, a scrumptious lunch in West Hollywood, California at Le Pain Quotidien with Captain Paul. I am thrilled that Captain Paul shared his evocative poetry throughout *Shepherding the Sea*. I wish to sincerely thank Dr Helen Caldicott, Laurie David, Jeff Hansen, Dr Stephen Johnson, Dr Douglas Larson, Chris Maser, Bill McKibben, Dr David Perry, Dr Rollin Richmond, Dr John Ryan, Dr Robert Teskey, Dr Roger Sands, Gerry Schwartz, Dr Christopher Weston, Robyn Williams and Alex Witt for reading the manuscript and providing splendid testimonials. I also wish to thank Mark White of Byron Bay, NSW and Adam Burling, Media Coordinator of Sea Shepherd Australia for introducing me to Dr Bob Brown. In the midst of writing his own memoir, *Optimism*, Bob Brown accepted my invitation and wrote a smashing *Foreword* for *Shepherding the Sea*. Dr Dave Randle of University of South Florida has championed ocean conservation for decades and kindly invited me to work on several fascinating ocean projects during 2012 and 2013 in St Petersburg, Fla. Thanks Dr Dave. I'd like to extend my heartfelt gratitude to Jeff and June Louks for the grand opportunity in August 2013 of engaging brilliant young minds at the Malibu Leadership Academy. I'd also like to acknowledge my friend Ron Bernardo for his inspiration during the latter part of this exciting project. I am very grateful for Bob Arnold's passion and support of *Earth Calling SOS* at its inception. Brian Schremp joined *Earth Calling SOS* in March of 2014 and has masterfully produced all the videos as well as producing the audio book *Shepherding the Sea*. Thank you, Brian. Dr Michael Read of The Level has provided exceptional web-based support for over a decade-and-a-half, and I am most obliged for all his efforts. I asked, on very short notice, my childhood friend, Phil "Cousteau" Ashdown, to undertake the editorial task of making this manuscript into an excellent read. I am indeed very grateful for his friendship, counsel and excellence. My publicist Warren Betts is to be congratulated for his love of bees, trees and our seas, and all his tireless work to protect our environment. For Jeff King, Head of MUSE School CA, Suzy Amis-Cameron and Rebecca Amis, cofounders of MUSE School CA, thank you for allowing my passion to enrich all the students at "the coolest school on the planet!" I wish to extend a sincere thank you to Anita Matusevics-Halter of Wonder Inc. for undertaking the layout and smart design of this tremendous project.

Lastly, for all those who have heard "No" a couple million times in their pursuit of passion and excellence, remember this: "No, means go away and regroup!"

For the Oceans

27 September 2014
Los Angeles, California
Earth Dr Reese Halter

Foreword

Dr Reese Halter's *Shepherding the Sea* challenges everyone on Earth to stop ignoring the rape of the oceans, to end the age of marine plunder and to reserve and protect 80 per cent of the beleaguered seas. Halter describes the current plunder as "one of the darkest and most contemptible moments in the fleeting history of the human race."

Shepherding the Sea is also the testimony of Paul Watson, the greatest ocean defender alive. Watson's philosophy is as logical as it is revolutionary. With 90 per cent of the world's fisheries in collapse, he notes that "the global slaughter of marine wildlife is simply the largest massacre of wildlife on the planet. If the oceans die we will all die." With the United Nations World Charter for Nature at his side, Watson tells Halter simply and directly, "I am a warrior of the Earth." So he is, as are his global marine protection forces of Sea Shepherds. We are all challenged to go with them.

Meantime, Watson's marine law enforcers are spread thinly around the globe and corrupt or culpable governments are wagging their fingers at Sea Shepherd demanding it be nice to the plunderers like the illegal and bloody Japanese whaling fleet marauding Antarctica's International Whale Sanctuary.

Reese Halter points out that most of the big sea creatures have gone, most of the greatest concentrations of sea life are stuffed, and every living sea creature carries human-made chemicals. Yet seven billion citizens of the planet remain sitting back, while 44,000 factory ships are out there 24/7/365 smashing up what is left. We treat the ocean as a garbage dump for plastics and heavy metals. Our cats are fed more tuna than all the seals in the seas. Pigs now eat more fish than sharks. Our avoidable fleece jackets discard 1,900 micro-plastic fibres to the ocean every time we put them through the washing machine.

Halter lays the oceans' cards on the table: the result is a Marine Dooms-day Book. "Soon all that will be left is jellyfish and plankton. Japan, incidentally, is already buying over 30,000 kilograms (66,139 pounds) of jellyfish a week, turning it into slender wafers."

But that Doomsday doesn't have to be. Paul Watson is a living prescription for rescuing the seas and ourselves. His Sea Shepherd crews have captured the global imagination by tackling the illegal plunderers of whales, fishes, seabirds and krill. Watson advocates an international agency to enforce marine protection and uphold the World Charter of Nature.

Watson says there is no room for self-pity (he has suffered the plunderers' ire), that we cannot afford the luxury of pessimism, and that children are natural ecologists. No one is doing more or better than him to replace pessimism with inspiration so that these natural ecologists of the future will, with all of us backing them, carry through the historic task of saving of the seas.

—Dr Bob Brown

End of a Bloody Poacher

On the early afternoon of July 15, 1979, a courageous 29-year-old Earth warrior, Paul Watson, on board
a former North Sea trawler called the *Sea Shepherd*,
sighted the notorious whale-poaching vessel *Sierra,* 180
nautical miles from the coast of Portugal. "You murdering bastard," bellowed the passionate Watson. "You've
killed your last whale!" The search was finally over. The
hunter became the hunted. The chase was on.

The day before, somewhere on the Atlantic between the
Bay of Biscay and the African coast, *Sea Shepherd*
had encountered thousands of Loggerhead sea turtles.
These magnificent long-lived beauties glide through
the water as gracefully as albatross float through the air,
so noteworthy a sight and remarkable that, after four decades on the seven seas, Watson has since to experience
anything remotely similar. *Sea Shepherd* shut down her
engines and for six hours Watson and all the crew swam
and floated with these tremendous turtles of the sea.

At that moment, Watson had only one burning desire: "I was put on this Earth to send *Sierra* to the bottom. If I accomplish nothing else in my life, ending the career of that one vessel will have sufficed to give it meaning."

He was convinced that, had *Sea Shepherd* not encountered those Loggerheads and stopped, they would not have found *Sierra*. After all they had no previous sighting of her and trying to locate one ship in the North Atlantic without over the horizon assistance was analogous to finding a needle in a huge haystack. In fact, Watson believes those sea turtles were a guidepost sent from his friend Leonard Crow Dog, Papa Sapa in Black Hills, South Dakota, a shaman of the Oglala Rosebud. Turtles are a sacred symbol of the Sioux medicine and wheel of life.

In 1973, Watson and David 'Walrus' Garrick drove in a pickup truck from Vancouver, British Columbia, to South Dakota to join the American Indian Movement at Wounded Knee. They crawled over snow and ice on their stomachs past the F.B.I., U.S. Marshalls and National Guard Troops. Watson volunteered as a medic where, during the 69-day siege, two Indians were killed and one federal Marshall was badly wounded.

After the siege, in a vision at the Sweat Lodge Ceremony, a spirit guide spoke to Watson, revealing his destiny to protect the great whales, seals, wolves, elephants and eagles, preventing their extermination. He was accepted as a friend and warrior brother, given the name *Grey Wolf Clear Water* by the Oglala Lakota Nation.

On December 5, 1978, Cleveland Amory, President of Funds for Animals and the Royal Society for the Prevention of Cruelty to Animals, assisted Watson's newly formed Sea Shepherd Conservation Society by providing funding to procure *Westella*, a former Yorkshire deep-water trawl boat built in 1960. On Christmas Day, 1978, she was cleaned, painted, 40 tons of rocks were added for ballast and 18 tons of concrete were placed in her bow, bringing her weight to a respectable 779 tonnes (859 tons). She was renamed *Sea Shepherd*. Watson proudly proclaimed: "The whales now have a navy."

Sierra, on the other hand, was a deplorable whale poacher that worked 24/7 killing at least 10 majestic whales each day. She had already massacred at least 25,000 whales, many illegally. Run by Norwegian directors who exported prime meat to Nissui, Tokyo and second-grade meat to the UK for pet foods. *Sierra* was taken-over in 1972 by South African Andrew Behr and registered in Freetown, Sierra Leone. In 1975, *Sierra* was caught on film slaughtering endangered Humpback whales, protected 12 years earlier by the International Whaling Commission (IWC).

On June 22, 1979, US Senators Bob Packwood and Warren G. Magnuson co-chaired a hearing before the Committee on Commerce, Science & Transportation on Whaling Operations Conducted Outside the Control of the IWC. The hearing, at its very outset, identified *Sierra* as the number one pirate whale-poaching vessel on the high seas.

On the morning of July 16, 1979, *Sea Shepherd* had stalked its hapless prey, *Sierra*, into the port of Leixoes, in northern Portugal. Watson compensated Captain David Seller then discharged him. He turned to the remaining crew and asked them: "Are you willing to risk your life and go to jail for the sinking of the *Sierra*? If not, I'll pay your passage home." Fourteen of the sixteen disembarked. Chief engineer Peter Woof and third engineer Jerry Doran remained. The kill was set to happen.

An intrepid Captain Paul Watson took the helm of *Sea Shepherd* leaving Leixoes without the Harbour Master's permission, setting his sights on the brazen poachers. Watson was not ashamed that morning to admit'."I was deeply afraid, so much so that I could hardly speak because of the dryness in my throat. I was fearful of failing to carry out the mission, fearful of dying and most of all fearful of spending the rest of my life in a Portuguese prison."

His adrenaline coursed throughout every vein in his body like nothing the young Watson had ever known.

He picked up the marine radio and growled, "*Sierra, Sierra*. Goddam you, you whale-killing son-of-a-bitch, your career is going to end today!" He headed directly for her at 10 knots. He could see the faces of the whalers as they laughed and pointed. He aimed for her harpoon. The distance grew shorter, the Earth warrior let out a *Hoka Hey Lakota* "It's a good day to die." Three seconds later *Sea Shepherd* struck *Sierra*. Although it was a glancing blow, which caused minimal damage to the harpoon deck, Watson shouted, "Now we're going for your throat!" He spun round, doing a 360 behind *Sierra*'s stern, and *Sea Shepherd* came at 15 knots full on at a slight right angle towards *Sierra's* forward port side. *Sierra* was like a headlight-stunned deer on an Interstate Highway. As *Sea Shepherd* grew closer Watson could see the horrified amazement on the faces of the pirate whalers. He saw Captain Arvid Nordengen, the big Norwegian Skipper, standing, staring speechless, as helpless as the thousands of whales he routinely murdered. Watson recalls briefly glimpsing a poacher's rifle being raised toward him, but then 779 tonnes (859 tons) drove full force into *Sierra*. "We hardly felt the impact on board *Sea Shepherd*. We tore a two by two and a half-meter (7.2 x7.2 feet) hole into the pirate whaler and as we pulled out, we slammed full against her port side, staving in 14 metres (46 feet) of hull," exclaimed Watson.

The wounded *Sierra* immediately headed for port whilst *Sea Shepherd* began its four-hour run for freedom. But 13 kilometres (8 miles) from Spanish waters a Portuguese destroyer intercepted, then escorted, her to the nearest Portuguese port of Porto. The next day Watson and his two remaining crew appeared in front of the Harbour Master charged with criminal negligence. The only problem was that the owners of *Sierra* could not be determined. They were found "Not Guilty." They were free to go.

Sierra's insurers refused to pay $1 million in damages inflicted on its hull. The Portuguese courts awarded *Sea Shepherd* as compensation to the whalers unless Sea Shepherd Conservation Society paid a fine of $775,000. So on December 29, 1979, under the cover of night, Watson and Peter Woof arrived in Porto, snuck onto *Sea Shepherd*, entered the engine room, removed the bolts holding the seawater valve in place, and scuttled her.

Meanwhile *Sierra's* owners spent $1 million to repair the pirate ship. On the evening of February 6, 1980, two unknown men placed limpet mines on the hull of *Sierra*, sending her, once and for all, to the bottom of the Lisbon harbour.

Captain Paul Franklin Watson of the Sea Shepherd Conservation Society passionately believes: "To save the whales is to save the seas, and to save the seas is to save humanity."

An Ailing Life Support System

What if one morning you awoke and three out of every four breaths of air were unavailable? Our oceans, the cradle of life, not only supply us wherever you live on the globe with vital oxygen, food, potent medicines, energy, inspiration for the latest greatest products and technologies, but they are also home for the great whales, sharks, sea turtles, seabirds, tuna and at least another million species most of which have yet to be discovered. Over the last 50 years, mercury toxicity has tripled in our oceans to over 80,000 tonnes (88,145 tons) of poison. Eighty four per cent of fish tested are laced with methylmercury. The lion's share of mercury poison comes each year from burning in excess of 8 billion tonnes (8.8 billion tons) of coal to provide energy to electricity grids. Our oceans are in terrible trouble and this exposé is all about Earth's ailing life support system.

This book is written from my understanding of over a quarter century in the field of conservation biology, having studied nature in both hemispheres, and from my lengthy interviews with Captain Paul F. Watson of Sea Shepherd Conservation Society. Sea Shepherd is a global conservation movement of volunteers empowered by The United Nations (UN) World Charter for Nature protecting all sea life including seals, sea lions, sea turtles, albatross, tuna, sharks, seahorses, dolphins and the great whales from nefarious international poachers.

About 125 years ago, John Muir, the co-founder of the Sierra Club, walked from the US Midwest to Yosemite, California. He spent a couple years in Yosemite observing nature. I strongly recommend for those who have not read Muir to do so. His observations and writings are magnificent. Through his curiosity, reverence, powers of observation and assimilation, Muir became a renowned ecologist. He studied patterns on the landscape and over time understood them. Watson has spent a lifetime on the seas and his detailed observations of sea life patterns, and conclusions are precise, so much so that the National Oceanic and Atmospheric Administration's (NOAA) first female director in 1990, the eminent oceanographer, Dr Silvia Earle, fully concurs: "If the sea is sick, we feel it. If it dies, we die. Our future and the state of the oceans are one."

For those unfamiliar with the power of large numbers growing rapidly, at even a small rate of growth, allow me to draw your attention to the human population. Paleo-man emerged from the last Ice Age about ten thousand years ago. It took eighty-two hundred years, or until the year 1800, before our population reached one billion. In the year 1900, London was the largest city on the globe with a population of six-and-a-half million people. By 1930 our species reached two billion. By 1980 that number doubled to four billion and by 2011 we surpassed seven billion people.

As a conservation biologist I, too, study ecological systemic patterns within nature. Since 2009, I have carefully recorded some shocking global events including the death of half a trillion honeybees, a central link in our food production chain, as well as the monumental unintended consequences of burning in excess of 98.6 million tonnes (109 million tons) of greenhouse gases daily, notably the death of over 30 billion mature pines across the entire western North American continent. The planet has lost some of the finest carbon dioxide (CO_2) warehouses to have ever evolved. Billions of trees are decaying *en masse*, emitting gigatons of CO_2 into the atmosphere rather than storing it.

Human fingerprints are all over the seas. Since the 1950s, human-induced climate change has disrupted the deep ocean currents, preventing some upwelling carrying essential nutrients to the surface to grow phytoplankton (which provides humans with oxygen, among other things), the basis of the entire marine ecosystem. The oceans are missing 40 per cent of their phytoplankton. By 2024, according The UN Food & Agriculture Organization (FAO), there will be eight billion people on Earth. That's an immense amount of additional oxygen required just for them to breathe.

Scientists from the US National Center for Atmospheric Research (NCAR) have recently re-analyzed ocean temperatures from 1958 to 2009, noting that at least 30 per cent of Earth's warming was hidden by oceans, mixed by winds and currents to depths exceeding 700 metres (2,297 feet). The results are striking changes in the surface winds reflected by changing ocean currents that helped carry some of the warmer water down below 700 metres (2,297 feet). Not only is this highly visible in the tropical Pacific Ocean and into the subtropics, it is also driving weather patterns. Deep ocean warmer temperatures have begun surfacing in the Eastern Australian Current and elsewhere. Climate disruption is ravaging every ecosystem in the ocean including lambasting Tasmania's east coast kelp forests, which, in less-than-a-decade, are almost gone. Ninety-five per cent of the 30-metre (98-feet) tall underwater jungles are dead. Ocean temperatures have risen four times faster there than the mean global average. Warm, nutrient-poor water has brought 40 new species of fish south along with

the Long-spined sea urchins that devoured the kelp forests. Without the kelp forests there are no sponges, nor
fish especially adapted to its habitat. That ecosystem has
collapsed.

Nowhere is climate disruption more evident than in the
Arctic Ocean. Its plankton is dangerously close to releasing more CO_2 than it can absorb. The plankton communities 650 kilometres (404 miles) north of mainland
Europe on Svalbard Island are reaching temperatures
near 5C (41F). Once they cross this threshold, in scientific parlance, the plankton switches from a sink (absorbing CO_2) to a source (releasing CO_2). The University of Western Australia Ocean Institute predicts those
5C (41F) temperatures will regularly be reached later
this decade in the European sector of the Arctic Ocean.
Moreover, scientists from Dartmouth College in New
Hampshire revealed that the trillions of pieces of plastic trapped in Arctic ice are now being released into the
world's oceans as global warming melts the polar cap.

Every day, our oceans are currently attempting to digest over 38.5 million tonnes (42.4 million tons) of
CO_2 and it has now reached a tipping point, whereby,
marine physiologists, neuroscientists, pharmacologists,
and behavioural psychologists have revealed a shocking
outcome from the immense increase of CO_2 uptake in
our oceans: anxious fish that are loosing their ability to

detect the correct chemical cues. In the ocean off Papau New Guinea, fish are oddly becoming attracted to the smell of predators, a maladaptive response. Those confused fish are venturing further away from shelter thus becoming more exposed to predators. The high levels of CO_2 are actually interfering with the fundamental neurotransmitters in the brain of fish, causing them to take unnecessary and dangerous risks. Moreover, as the oceanic phytoplankton absorbs rising levels of CO_2, converting the sun's energy into green cells (the most perfect manufacturing system that I'm aware of), oxygen is released into the atmosphere and a weak carbonic acid is released into the sea as a byproduct of this reaction. To give you some idea how quickly Earth's life support systems are being forced by global warming, when I wrote *The Insatiable Bark Beetle* in 2011, that weak carbonic acid, according to the top marine and atmospheric laboratories, was changing the ocean's pH faster than anything in the record of the past 65 million years. Today, three years later, the revised rates show that the oceans are now acidifying faster than the previous 300 million years.

This is horrible news for all sea life, in particular for coral reefs and all shellfish (including krill), because they are made up of calcium carbonate, which melts under acidic conditions. Already acidity in the Pacific Ocean is killing off scallops according to British Columbia's

Shellfish Growers' Association where, in June of 2013, they lost 95 per cent of their crops. Acidifying oceans, by the way, will reverberate throughout the entire marine ecosystem causing a total collapse. Although they occupy less than one tenth of one per cent of ocean area globally, coral reefs brim with biodiversity, being home to at least one quarter and perhaps as much as a third of all known fish or about 8,000 to 10,600 species. Coral reefs support more species per square kilometre than any other marine environment, providing habitat, food, spawning and nursery grounds. At least 500 million humans depend on coral reefs for food, coastal protection and ecotourism, a net economic value of at least $30 billion per annum. Alarmingly, warming seas and acidity have killed at least 50 per cent of all coral reefs; the mortality rate may be as high as 80 per cent in the Caribbean Sea. In Australia the decline on the largest reef on the globe, the Great Barrier Reef, is almost 80 per cent on coastal and mid-shelf reefs in the central and southern regions. Paul Watson told me: "From March to November, of 2013, I saw vast areas of the Great Barrier Reef that were entirely dead." The April 2014, UN report from the Intergovernmental Panel on Climate Change, warned that the coral reefs are "the most valuable marine ecosystems on Earth." Global warming is killing them quickly. Coral reefs are to biodiversity in the ocean what the Amazon rainforests is to the land: Hotbeds of life.

In order to overcome a lack of nutrients, corals evolved an elegant symbiotic relationship with zooanthellae – a photosynthetic algae that lives within the coral polyps. Corals are made up of duodecillion polyps, resembling miniature sea anemones, a couple millimetres long. Individual polyps live in a small cup-shaped skeleton of calcium carbonate, which it makes. Thousands of years of accumulation enable calcium carbonate to form coral reefs. Polyps draw energy from the algae living in their tissue and in return they supply algae with nitrogen and phosphorus. Moreover, algae recycle all the polyps' waste as a part of the photosynthesis process. There is no waste in nature. Never.

Massive sewage and agricultural runoff, rising water temperatures and acidifying oceans have caused the polyps to expel the zooanthellae and die. The corals then turn white in a ghastly process called bleaching. Habitat is irreparably destroyed. In parts of the Indonesian 'Coral Triangle,' over 450 species of coral and 2,800 kinds of fish including the recently discovered miniature 2-millimetre (0.08-inch) Pygmy Bargibant's and Denise's seahorses (whose males brood the young in a pouch located within the body cavity rather than on the their tails) have perished.

The relentless quest for coal is delivering the coup de grâce to Australia's marine wonder, which is on the brink of devastation. The rampant destruction of the Great Barrier Reef, the largest living organism on the planet, epitomizes the values of our modern world. "Economic development" and "jobs" reign supreme while our reef, one of the Seven Wonders of the World, a UNESCO World Heritage site, is in dire jeopardy.

It is home to 3,000 individual reefs with over 600 islands and 600 types of corals spread over 2,300 kilometres (1,429 miles) or about the size of Italy. It shelters over 1,500 kinds of fish, 134 species of sharks and rays and at least 30 species of whales and dolphins. It is also crucial habitat for gentle endangered dugongs and glorious endangered sea turtles. It is teaming with life rich in biodiversity containing many potential medications to treat cancer, pain and other diseases. The preservation of this unique treasure is now secondary to the voracious greed on the part of Queensland and federal governments and some individuals to export coal. By 2030, Australia is predicted to have increased its export of coal from 240 million tonnes (265 million tons) this year (2014), to 787 million tonnes (868 million tons) in 2030. Queensland's liquefied natural gas and coal exports are soaring in order to deliver atmospheric-warming carbon fuels to satisfy Chinese and Indian markets.

The ports of Gladstone and Abbot Point are poised

to become the busiest in the world. In 2011, the shipping industry alone increased Australia's export trade coffers by $38 billion. In 2012, 3,950 ships entered these Great Barrier Reef ports and these numbers are set to triple by 2030. A war is being conducted against nature on our reef. All countries, by international law, are required to protect and preserve rare or fragile ecosystems as well as the habitat of depleted, threatened or endangered species. But in Queensland, since the 1960s, the plant-eating dugong population has plummeted by over 97 per cent in the quest to feed ravenous energy markets and to promote urban coastal growth. Dugongs depend on sea grass meadows to provide them with food. Those saline meadows also offer crucial habitat for a wide array of plants and other sealife, including sea turtles. This fecund zone is of cardinal importance for not only cycling nutrients that sustain all coastal sealife, but also it protects the reef from land-based toxicity that enters the sea. The reef's magnificent natural shield has been impregnated. The acidification of the ocean as a result of global warming further compromises the structure of the corals.

Then there is the problem of noise. The Queensland and federal governments are aware that noise pollution can have a detrimental effect on oceanic wildlife including all the biological processes that take place within the reef itself. Whales, dolphins, sea turtles and Dugongs are at risk from noise pollution as they incur cardiovascular and autoimmune stresses. Animals ranging from Blue whales to the Coral clown fish, cease feeding and noise pollution prevents mating. Yet no government noise regulation has been imposed on industry to curtail the final death knell for Earth's greatest reef. The 2012 UN World Heritage meeting in Paris warned of the deadly consequences associated with increasing noise pollution of shipping, sub-sea construction and the use of exploratory oil and gas sonar which causes mass stranding of whales and dolphins. The UN Convention on the Law of the Sea states that all countries are to lessen under sea noise pollution, including vessel noise and sub-sea construction equipment. The ongoing damage to reef is extraordinary. To create three liquefied natural gas terminals on Curtis Island near Gladstone, 21 million tonnes (23.1 million tons) of material were dredged. This irreparably destroyed the seabed, enormous plumes of sediment were released, fish were killed *en masse* and the bund wall containing land-dumped dredging was breached, causing a vast toxic algal bloom. UNESCO has now threatened to list the Great Barrier Reef as a World Heritage in Danger site.

These developments signal the beginning of ongoing massive port constructions adjacent to the Great Barrier Reef. What are we doing in the face of this catastrophe? We are devastating an extraordinarily beautiful natural wonder so we can heat up the planet and, in the process, destroy most forms of life.

I spent late spring of 2010 reporting the BP Deepwater Horizon blowout in the Gulf of Mexico for New York's MSNBC television, the Atlanta Journal-Constitution and Austin's America-Statesman. Over 794-million litres (210 million gallons) of oil with high concentrations of methane gushed into the Gulf. The pollution was fatal for all marine life including the critically endangered Eastern Atlantic Bluefin tuna and its breeding grounds, ruinous for oyster farmers and tourism throughout the Gulf. I was particularly concerned for Florida's coral reefs, home to sponges containing cancer medicines that helped prolong my mother's life after the onset of leukaemia. The solution to pollution is not dilution. Seven million litres (1.8 million gallons) of Corexit oil dispersant were pumped into the Gulf and detected on some of the Floridian coral reefs that subsequently died.

As coral reefs are harmed or destroyed, we lose the potential to discover the powerful medicines that come from them. For instance, researchers have discovered that the toxic venom from the poisonous *Conus magus* Sea snail that lives in the coral reefs in the Philippines is a naturally perfect compound for treating pain. Synthetically recreated, this compound is now the blockbuster pain medication Prialt (ziconotide), which is 100 times stronger than morphine and, unlike morphine, considered non-addictive. Beyond that, soft corals from northwestern Australia are the most efficacious anti-cancer compounds ever found, and Caribbean sea squirts are used to treat melanoma and breast cancers. Since 1969, sponges from the Florida Keys have played a valuable role in treating leukaemia, and it was research into these that led scientists to develop the important AIDS drug AZT. Coral is the most effective treatment in regrowing human bones, with patients requiring no immunosuppressing drugs. Incidentally, ocean-derived pharmaceuticals are so important that Merck, Lilly, Pfizer, Hoffmann-La Roche and Bristol-Myers Squibb have all established marine biology divisions. The ecosystem services that healthy, vibrant coral reefs provide us has been estimated at $1-trillion annually. Coral reefs are our children's legacy.

Twenty one per cent of the globe, except in Japan where it's 43 per cent, rely on the sea for their daily source of protein. Overfishing is so rampant that the oceans are fished-out. Deep sea trawling is so damaging that my colleagues have likened the physical destruction of 3,000-year-old seamount corals and all seabeds to that of 150 times greater than clear-cutting forests on the land. Each year, fisheries and poachers are killing the equivalent volume of sea life to fill 122 Empire State

Buildings (at 103-stories with a roof height of 381 metres or 1,250 feet) or one building every 2.9 days!

Watson puts it this way: "Fish act as the natural glue that keeps marine ecosystems in place. They ensure that the oceans continue to function. If the fish disappear the oceans die. If the oceans die, we die." As if this weren't shocking enough, the voracious demands by over 300 million *nouveau riche* Chinese are decimating all species of shark for their fins, served in sharkfin soup. In less than two decades humans will have exterminated all sharks and rays, which, until very recently, stood the phenomenal test of 400 million years of evolution.

America alone consumes over 39 billion disposable, petroleum-based plastic beverage bottles, annually. Australians consume over 600 million disposable plastic water bottles each year. Our oceans are a polluted broth of plastic in their entirety. As we shall see throughout this exposé, "What we do to the oceans we do to ourselves." We have bludgeoned over 50 million Harp seals, harpooned over five million whales and nearly wiped-out the superlative Leatherback turtles in the Pacific Ocean.

My colleagues worldwide are apprehensive, as are Watson and I. Earth's life support system – our oceans – are ailing, desperately. There's a bloody and ruthless

"War Against Nature," taking place 24/7, the destruction of nature and trafficking of animal parts using children as slave labour especially in the fishing industry is valued in excess of $400 billion, annually. It now rivals that of drugs, arms and human trafficking, combined. The fact that the Mafia, Syndicate, Yakuza, Cartel and Triads are heavily involved means they are hastening the demise of life, as we know it. It must end, now. We are running perilously out of time – inaction is obviously unacceptable. The late famed explorer and inventor of the aqua-lung Jacque-Yves Cousteau once said, "People protect what they love. To love something you must get to know it." To this Watson and I add, with knowing comes caring and respect for life in the sea, because without everyone becoming aware and lending a helping hand to heal our oceans, the human race will perish.

Who is Captain Paul Franklin Watson?

To over 3.4 million Animal Planet television Southern and Northern Hemisphere citizens – Captain Paul Watson is the courageous and tactful leader of the Sea Shepherd Conservation Society, the star of "Whale Wars." The show is entering its seventh consecutive season. The goal of protecting the remaining great whales of the Southern Ocean Sanctuary is working as David (Sea Shepherd) so far has stopped Goliath (Japan) due to the International Court of Justice (ICJ) ruling that on March 31, 2014 upheld Australia's bid to ban Japanese whaling in the Antarctic Ocean. Despite this landmark legal ruling, Japan intends on returning so this treacherous life and death match is set to resume, but more about that later on.

Sea Shepherd devised a clever and effective strategy whereby their fleet of boats (in 2013 there were three) chased down the Japanese whalers, preventing them from transferring the harpooned whales onto the industrialised factory ship *Nisshin Maru*. They do this by blocking the slip sternway, impeding the transfer and loading of dead whales to be processed. In 2006, Sea Shepherd saved 83 whales, in 2007 about 500, and 2008, 305 in 2009, 528 in 2010, 863 in 2011, 768, in 2012, 932 and 2013, 784. Between 2006 and 2013, Sea Shepherd saved 7,513 Southern Ocean whales.

So, who is Captain Paul Franklin Watson? And why do 100,000 supporters donate over $11 million annually to one of the most successful and well run direct-action global conservation movement of volunteers on the planet?

Watson is a remarkable combination of Tom Sawyer, Robin Hood, John Muir, Samuel Coleridge, and Captain George Vancouver with a twist of Sir Ernst Shackleton and a sprinkle of Farley Mowat. Born on December 2, 1950 in Toronto, Ontario his love of nature was evident very early on, growing up along the shores of the Bay of Fundy in New Brunswick on Canada's east-coast where Cod, Harp seals and beavers were all still plentiful. Watson relished the opportunities to explore nature along the coast and throughout its forests. It was, in his reflections, an idyllic childhood. Even at a young age he abhorred the brutality and mistreatment of wild or domesticated animals. At the age of eight, he mailed off for a membership in the Kindness Club, an organization that promoted the humane treatment of animals. During the summers he enlisted his brothers and sisters to set critters free from traps as they roamed the nearby forests.

Looking back now, five and half decades later, Watson vividly sees that children intuitively love animals and nature. "I can guarantee that a six-year-old child is more aware of what is happening in the world than the average adult. But we quash that passion. And that's what we lose when we become adults," says Watson, a father himself.

A couple summers after joining the Kindness Club, Watson came across a beaver pond, spending hours marveling at the engineering tour de force of the dam and the indefatigable work of the beavers as they fastidiously harvested twigs and small branched, building a crib of green food on the bottom of the pond to sustain them for the following winter. Watson swam in that pond, winning the trust of the beavers. At an incredibly tender age of eleven Watson intuitively learned to become one with nature. That characteristic has remained untarnished at his core throughout his life.

Soon after befriending the beavers, Watson witnessed the bludgeoning and skinning-alive of a Harp seal – so brutal and indelibly burned into his psyche, he vowed to avenge that blood lust. Passion, courage and imagination stand strong with him to this very day from that heinous act witnessed in 1961.

There was one other notable incident, that occurred during his formative years, shaping his character, preparing him for the forthcoming decades. One day when playing with a couple of children he was tricked, tied-up in an old abandoned boat, left to die with the rising tide. He struggled, screamed and eventually came to stare into the eyes of death as the tidal water rose higher and higher. Like any survivalist in an emergency knows, panic can kill you within minutes. Somehow young Watson calmed himself, managed to wriggle his hands free from the tightly bound ropes, quickly untying his feet, narrowly escaping death by drowning from the legendary high tides of the Bay of Fundy. That near-death experienced empowered him, strengthened his character with nerves of steel and taught him not ever to fear death.

Watson left home at fifteen, journeyed west to the Pacific coast of British Columbia and ran off to sea, joining the Norwegian merchant marine. For the next few years of his life he served in the Swedish merchant marine, the Canadian Coast Guard and for Canadian Pacific Steamship Lines. Upon returning to British Columbia he enrolled at Simon Fraser University in Burnaby, studying linguistics and communications. There he became familiar with film, studying Marshall McLuhan and the new planet wide mass communication system or what McLuhan referred to in the late 1960s as the "electronic global village." Watson would use McLuhan's concepts very effectively in the near future. Also, during this time he began refining his craft of writing with the Georgia Strait, a counter-culture weekly.

In 1970, Watson became the youngest member of the Greenpeace Foundation. He sailed on the first voyage to protest nuclear weapons testing in the Aleutians in 1971. And in June, 1975, a 25-year-old Watson was the first mate on a former halibut seiner flying the Greenpeace rainbow flag, chasing the Soviet whaling fleet about 60 nautical miles from Eureka, California.

In one of the most evocative stories that I've ever read, Watson recalls that day as "the greatest gift he'd ever received and also his great and enduring curse." In a small dingy with an outboard motor, he and Bob Hunter (one of the Greenpeace co-founders) tried to protect eight Sperm whales. The bloodthirsty Soviets harpooned a female Sperm whale right in front of them and her bloodcurdling scream was so human-like to this day it remains fresh in Watson's mind. A male Sperm whale sprang out of the water in defense of the dying female, likely his mate, attempting to attack the harpooner on the 46-metre (151-foot) Soviet whaling vessel. The gunner shot the bull in the head. The Sperm whale went into violent contortions. It surfaced right over their dingy, sparing Watson and Hunter's lives. As it lay beside the dingy Watson peered into its eyes. That the whale could have killed him but didn't, changing the course of Watson's life forever. As Watson recounts, "I saw understanding in its eyes. He understood what we were trying to do. I also saw pity in his eyes. Pity for us humans, who are able to kill without mercy. Why were the Russians killing whales? They were hunting the Sperm whales to obtain spermaceti, a lubricating oil that can withstand high temperatures. Spermaceti is used to manufacture intercontinental ballistic missiles, among other things. We were killing these magnificent, extremely intelligent and socially complex creatures in order to manufacture weapons of mass destruction so that we can kill one another. Something in me changed that day. From that time forward, I stopped doing things for people and started working exclusively for whales and other marine creatures."

Greenpeace captured some of the Soviet whaling on camera and footage of Watson swimming over to the dead female, kneeling on her back. His picture appeared in newspapers worldwide the next morning. In San Francisco, he was interviewed on television, it was wall-to-wall media coverage as Watson had entered into the "electronic global village."

In 1977, he returned on his second Greenpeace campaign to the ice floe off Newfoundland, Canada to intervene in the barbaric slaughter of Harp seal pups. He was dunked in the freezing Atlantic Ocean and then viciously beaten by the hunters, but his indomitable spirit rose up and overcame it. Watson masterminded Brigitte Bardot's arrival to the ice floe, and her picture holding a newborn white Harp seal. That one picture was seen by hundreds of millions of people, it influenced the European Common Market to ban Canadian Harp seal pup pelts. Watson saw that alarming images attracted media, galvanised public opinion and eventually they save entire species.

Later that year Watson, disenfranchised with growing Greenpeace bureaucracy, left the organisation and founded Sea Shepherd Conservation Society with support from "the founding father of the modern animal protection movement," his friend Cleveland Amory and the Fund for Animals. For almost four decades, Watson and his volunteer-only crew members who are willing to lay down their lives for the whales have accomplished what no other marine-based conservation movement could match – protection of sealife by direct-action. When asked why he prefers volunteers with a twinkle in his eyes he refers me to the experience recorded by Sir Ernst Shackleton, "I don't really want any professionals, I want men with enough passion to get me to the South Pole and bring me back."

In 37 years, Watson has sunk 9 whaling ships: *Sierra* in Portugal, four of Norway's at dock, *Astrid* in the Canary Islands, Iceland's whalers in Reykjavik harbour, half the Spanish fleet *Isha I* and *Isha II*, and he's never hurt anyone nor been convicted of a felony in any country. When it comes to all marine life but in particular the whales it is not hard to applaud his actions, after all there's only between 1 and 3 per cent of the whale populations left in the seas since the early 1800s.

From 1982 onward Watson and Sea Shepherd have been upholding international law under the UN World Charter for Nature, in particular:

Article 21. States and, to the extent they are able, other public authorities, international organisations, individual groups and corporations shall:

(c) Implement the applicable international legal provisions for the conservation of nature and protection of the environment.

(e) Safeguard and conserve nature in areas beyond national jurisdiction.

Sea Shepherd is very good at what they do and that's why they are contracted by the Ecuadorian government to protect the gorgeous Galapagos marine life. Poaching along its Marine Reserve prior to Sea Shepherd's arrival was unbridled, mired in corruption. Six months after

Ecuadorian President bestowed Watson with the coveted Amazon Peace Prize for excellence in conservation, Sea Shepherd Director of Operations was arrested in the Galapagos because he arrested one of the President's friends. Irrespective of the layers of worldwide corruption, "Sea Shepherd has the right to defend the planet against criminals who destroy it for their own profit and greed," says Watson.

Watson outlines concisely the three inviolable laws of ecology:

The strength of any ecosystem is based on its biodiversity and he warns people rightfully, "The decreased level of biodiversity on the planet today is our most serious problem even more serious than global warming."

All species are interdependent and work in concert; and

The law of finite resources states that all growth has a limit and there is a limit to Earth's carrying capacity in terms of the number of humans.

After sailing the seas for more than four decades Watson, too, is deeply disturbed with "marine pollution (both chemical and plastic), habitat destruction (from intense over-fishing), industrial sprawl and an out of control human population." When I heard him say, "You know what the Japanese delegate Tadahiko Nakamura said to me at the 1997 IWC meeting in Monaco? He said, "He didn't care if all the whales died. He said his duty was to his family, his company, his country and, that it was his duty to harvest all the whales they could before they were all gone." I felt a deep pit in my gut. But Watson's never gets flustered, as I observed, because it's his unadulterated passion and belief that "The validity of our acts today will be judged by people who will not be born for hundreds of years. I am confident that history will absolve us – the conservationists, the animal rights movement – of the accusations and the libel of the spin doctors and the public relations companies representing industry and government." Watson is also quick to point out, "The fact is that we are going to lose more species of plants and animals between 2000 and 2065 than the planet has lost over the past 65 million years. We are at the height of a mass extinction crisis. This age of extinction is called the Anthropocene because *Homo sapiens* are responsible for it."

Like him, love him or otherwise Captain Paul Franklin Watson and his band of loyal followers are protecting your children's birthright – the living oceans. I, for one, couldn't agree more with him: "Spiritually, the protection of Earth's ecosystems is the most moral and just cause ever taken up in the history of the human species."

His courage is legendary as exemplified by his poetry.

Deny Not Courage

By Captain Paul F. Watson

Heed not the strength of those who oppose you
The strength of any army is finite
The powers of governments are finite
Although the forces of justice are few
Social movements have always started small
Persistence, patience, purpose and passion
Consideration, courage, compassion,
Cultivate these virtues and you stand tall
And dare to go where none say you may not
Speak, act and stand fast with courageous grace
Your own conscience is always your best guide
For we know despite what we have been taught
Failure to intervene is a disgrace
Courage can never ever be denied.

Wonders of the Sea

When was the last time that you stood at the sea's edge, gazed out upon the aqua marine wavy, windy surface, and inhaled a bite of brine whilst the surf lapped at your feet? Ever wondered how the Gray whale, the longest migratory marine mammal, navigates without a map? Or that 39-tonne (43-ton) Humpback whales sing, not just to attract mates, but also for their supper or, at least, while they hunt for it? Or, that when a fish is hooked it feels excruciating pain just like a human?

The sea is mysterious and it's Earth's final unexplored frontier. Would you believe that science knows far more about the face of the moon and the surface of Mars compared to bottom of our oceans? We know less than one tenth of one per cent of the deep ocean surface. In March of 2012, famed film producer and explorer James Cameron and crew journeyed in *Deepsea Challenger* submarine to the Mariana Trench, *Challenge Deep* located 320 kilometres (199 miles) southwest of Guam to the very bottom of over 10,924 metres (35,840 feet), more than a kilometre-and-a-half (one mile) greater than Mt. Everest. Cameron and his team brought back high-resolution 3D images and footage of unprecedented clarity, collected sediment, physical oceanographic data and biological samples. Analysis of that data has lead to the discovery of 68 new species of life. So just how many animals, plants and other oceanic life forms are archived at the Smithsonian Institute in Washington, DC? Currently, there are over 226,000 kinds of marine life that scientists have recorded including 20,000 new species in the last decade, alone.

Our blue planet is unquestionably breathtaking when viewed from outer space. The oceans occupy about 70 per cent of Earth's surface and they account for over 95 per cent of the biosphere, the planet's living space. The deepest point is 10.92 kilometres (6.8 miles) with 1,092 crushing atmospheric pressures, yet the tenacious will of life has found a way to cope even there in total darkness. We have explored less than five per cent of our oceans. It is exhilarating to know that as hunters and gatherers, the human brain is hard-wired for wonder and awe. That one fact may be humanities saving grace when it comes to protecting the seas for our children.

Life began 3.5 billion years ago. Ultraviolet (UV) radiation relentlessly bombarded the planet. The thin atmosphere was a deadly mixture of hydrogen, ammonia, methane, and carbon monoxide with very little or no free oxygen. Did life first occur along a deep-sea volcanic vent? Or was it in a warm, shallow lagoon? Or was it from a bolt of lightning, striking the ocean's surface? Lightning was a major force in that world of very active volcanic upheavals, and it could easily ignite the recombination of deoxyribonucleic acids (DNA), the main constituent of chromosomes, which carry genetic code. DNA is the fundamental building blocks of life, with the power to replicate itself as the blueprint for the formation of amino acids (the back-bone of proteins). The oldest forms of life (and the first fossils) bacteria, fed on carbon compounds accumulated in the seas. Over time, it made its own food from free hydrogen released from volcanic activity. Miraculously, there came a time when this blue-green algae developed the ability to harvest the sun's energy, using CO_2 in primitive green or chloro cells, thus making its own food. One major byproduct of this stunning process was the release of oxygen.

So much oxygen was released that some oxygen floated to the upper atmosphere and formed Earth's ozone layer. That remarkable oxygen-rich layer filters and prevents most of the sun's UV radiation from reaching the Earth. Once this ozone layer was in place, life on our planet took off. First, in the oceans as oxygen levels rose above 0.1 per cent (about 800 million years ago) then from the oceans onto land, life proliferated. Today, off the coasts of East Africa and Western Australia there is what looks like worn-out old stumps called stromatalites, containing evidence of the first ancient bacteria dating to 3.5 billion years ago.

Oh, if we could turn the hands of time back just 10,000 years to listen to life in the sea. It was so melodious, filled with sounds that would convince you it was life from another galaxy. Life then in the sea was so vibrant, so abundant and so pure. Sounds like the signature high frequency sonic clicks of 236 decibels from the giant Sperm toothed-whales, the largest brain size (five times heavier than humans) of any creature to have lived on the planet, scanning the icy darkness for colossal squid lurking in the seas. Or a faster version of those communication clicks or codas, sounding identical to horses trotting on a hard, fast racetrack. Or you would have heard the unmistakable immense filter-feeding Blue whales, the champion and truest broadcasters with their low frequency calls at over 185 decibels: Short, powerful bursts analogous to 19th century Morse Code clearly audible on the other side of entire ocean basins, 5,000 kilometres (3,107 miles) away. At over 30 metres (98 feet) long, by the time Blue's tail leaves the surface for a deep dive, it's farther than most scuba divers will have ever ventured, into the ethereal abyss. I predict the sounds that would have intrigued you the most were the sonorous groans, the unearthly wails and the eloquent adagios of male Humpback whales serenading their mates, a song that changes and lasts continuously for as long as 22 hours. Or from the northern polar seas there were trills, chuckling, mewing like a stringed orchestra tuning-up, deep sighing, grunting, or, the distant sounds of a crowd of children playing, those would be some of the calls from the Arctic Beluga whales. Or, certainly you would be rapt by the subtle discharge of snaps, crackles and pops emanating from Western Australia's Ningaloo Reef, coming alive annually, resembling a pink underwater snow storm by numerous kinds of coral colonies all releasing their reproductive eggs at once, one week after the autumnal equinox full moon.

Profuse mats of green life, collectively known as phytoplankton, provide the basis of life in our oceans. They directly capture the sun's energy providing food and security cover for most marine life to occur. For instance, phytoplankton provides food for microscopic or other tiny forms of sealife called zooplankton. Of particular interest, and of paramount importance, is one of the 80 species of krill, a shrimp-like crustacean called Antarctica krill (*Euphansia superta*) that's drawn to the phytoplankton mats. These 50-millimetre (2-inch) long, pinkish-red creatures when mature possess huge black eyes, emitting a resplendent and eerie bright blue-green bioluminescence. Their existence is essential for the vitality of the web of life within the polar seas, particularly the Great Southern Ocean. They mature slowly, passing through no less than one dozen stages from egg to adult, each stage relying upon and feeding from the savoury plankton stew.

It takes almost two years for an individual Antarctic krill to mature and reproduce, and if not consumed by great whales, seals, penguins, albatrosses and petrels or squid, they can live for as long as 8 years. These protein-rich, loaded with omega-3 oil, little beauties are the single most numerous creatures in the sea having acquired enough energy to build the largest animals ever to exist on Earth: giant Blue whales. Before the onset of human-induced global warming, the growth of Antarctic krill, each year, in the Southern Ocean produced new material that weighed twice as much as all the sugar produced in the world.

Krill are imperative to the well-being of the entire marine ecosystem, worthy of global protection, not squandered for cattle, chicken, fish or pig feed or human supplements, nor ever eligible for any profligate fisheries subsidies. Dr Sylvia Earle calls the Antarctic krill "the linchpin – something humans do not want to tug upon." Since the 1970s, initially Soviets, and then many other countries, began mass harvesting krill by as much as half a billion tonnes (551 million tons), annually. As if over-harvesting wasn't stressful enough on the Southern Ocean marine ecosystem, global warming has blind-sided the krill by rapidly melting sea ice in the Western Antarctic, which provides (especially for larvae) essential over-winter habitat of sea ice algae and plankton their food sources. A recent British Antarctic Survey estimated that krill populations have crashed by as much as 80 per cent since the 1970s.

Globally, plankton forms the base of the marine food pyramid. Watson will remind you: "The strength of an ecosystem depends on the diversity of species." For example, plush mats of plankton offer microsites supporting animals and plants that include: schools of Herring, Menhaden, Shad, Pilchard, Whiting, Sardines, Anchovies, Pollock, squid and almost all juvenile fish stocks in the sea. Tuna, salmon, Dorado feed on schools of smaller fish. In turn, apex predators at the top of the food chain like Tiger sharks and Orcas feed on salmon and tuna. The fact that so much plankton is missing due to global warming and from intense over-harvesting of the sea, has become deeply troublesome for scientists observing all marine ecosystems unraveling at unprecedented rates.

The open oceans are far from void deserts as once believed. The astounding seafloor topography creates habitat for plankton and where there's plankton there's prolific sealife. Glorious submerged mountains known as seamounts jut upwards from the muddy seafloor. Only 1,000 of the estimated 50,000 in the Pacific Ocean have ever been named. Strong currents bathe seamounts and superb ancient sea coral gardens, sea fans and sponges carpet their summits. The corals filter and feed from the fast-moving ocean currents creating exquisite habitat, providing nutrients attracting phytoplankton, allowing fish, filter-feeding whales and all deep-sealife to prosper. Where there are smaller fish expect big predators like tuna, along a trans-Atlantic or -Pacific run, and squid that feed the superlative albatrosses.

It's not just the enormous likes of the spectacular Mariana chain, which runs 2,500 kilometres (1,553 miles) and at its widest point 69 kilometres (43 miles), east of Mariana Island near Japan, or the other spectacular global seamounts that offer necessary topography to sustain marine life. Big, ancient trees living along the Pacific North American coastline and elsewhere are vital links providing a carbon food source, nourishing the sea. Oregon scientists Chris Maser and Jim Sedell calculated that before paleo-humans, 21-million metres^3 (741-million feet^3) of big, dead, old trees traveled into estuaries from Alaska to northern California, annually. At over one per cent of an escape rate at least 210,000 metres^3 (7.4 million feet^3) entered the open Pacific Ocean each year. The decomposition of huge rainforest trees represents a cardinal phase for life in streams, rivers and oceans.

Known as driftwood, the trunk, roots and large branches of dead trees form tremendous dams, riffles and pools, creating backwater along forest streams and rivers, which is crucial habitat for both trout and salmon. That driftwood is the foundation for biological activities that spreads energy throughout the water, trapping newly created nutrient-rich sediments. These enormous trees may topple along the stream bank due to high spring runoff undercutting them. Or they might enter the waterway from areas fraught with gale force Pacific winds becoming windthrow along ridge-tops, carried by landslides and massive stream erosion during a one-in-50-year flood, adding millions of tonnes of woody debris to coastal streams.

Eventually that driftwood moves down streams or rivers into estuaries and out into the sea where it begins decomposing first by woodborers like gribbles and formidable shipworms (some which reach over 1.5 metres or 4.6 feet). Shipworms bore to grow and plow through wood like a red hot knife through butter, excreting fecal pellets serving as an imperative food source for flatworms, round worms and predatory snails living along the seafloor. Much of the driftwood in the North Pacific remains inshore due to the oscillating currents, however some big western redcedars, Sitka spruce, coastal redwoods and Douglas-firs enter the open ocean and the Great North Pacific Gyre, a vast circular vortex, one which carries driftwood to Hawaii and beyond. Driftwood at sea is quickly and heavily populated with plants, animals and including the only known insect to successfully invade the open ocean, the ocean strider. It lacks wings so it floats and skates on the surface of the sea, attaching its eggs to floating driftwood.

An individual piece of driftwood can have in excess of 100 species of invertebrates or spineless creatures and over 130 kinds of fish congregated on and around it. Having collected plankton and attracted first small fish, and then larger predatory fish such as Dorado and tuna, the combined weight of this ecosystem can easily weigh 85 tonnes (94 tons). Although the tuna and other predatory fish deplete their available prey quickly, they move away, using the driftwood as a point of reference, circling back to feed again and again.

Large driftwood is so important that tuna time their migration to the North Pacific continental shelf for spawning to coincide with monsoonal December to March rains as they, too, use the plankton mats associated with driftwood ecosystems for their eggs, requiring both security cover and food sources. Driftwood provides an indispensable habitat similar in so many ways to seamounts and reefs. Tuna fishermen learned about this 50 years ago and ever since they too have been on the look-out for big floating logs. How do tuna know where to find driftwood? It's not known but likely a combination of visual, olfactory and perhaps even sonic detection.

Driftwood floats for a couple years at sea eventually sinking and meeting its last woodborers, which convert all wood into fecal pellets, feeding nonillion seabed bot-tom-dwellers. Over-harvesting of big trees and deliber-ate removal of large driftwood by harbour patrols has eliminated this tuna habitat and prevented the seafloor from eating wood. Instead, humans have sentenced sea-life to digest a new mono-diet: Plastics.

For the first time in evolutionary history of deep-sea an-imals, the availability of wood, their food source, has become scarce. Mangrove forests are being dilapidated. Many of the creatures along the seabed, which have yet to be discovered along with known residents including the latest discovery by Scripps Institution of Ocean-ography of an antibiotic compound from microbes in the ocean floor mud, are being denied their food and facing extinction. In addition, dead sea creatures cover 98 per cent of the ocean floor area tested off Califor-nia's coast, up from one per cent since the tsunami of 11 March 2011 when the Fukushima nuclear reactors began leaking immense amounts of radiation into the

Pacific Ocean. This particular and eventual total extinction of species by denying them driftwood will have an immeasurable effect on seabed life. Big, old, dead trees that become driftwood inexorably link the forest to the sea thereby sustaining thousands of known unique terrestrial and marine species.

Of the approximately 32,000 species of fish in the sea, tunas are the pinnacle of piscine evolution, and Bluefin are the most advanced of them all: The ultimate predator. A Bluefin can accelerate faster than a Ferrari. Welcome to the zenith of evolution in the sea. Tuna is a fast moving marine fish, plump in the middle, pointed at both ends like a football. Their tail fin, or, caudal, is a crisp crescent shape. They are two-toned or counter-shaded, dark on the topside, light below; a colour scheme of blue, green and silver befitting their characterisation as "jet fighters of the sea."

There are eight species of tuna: Yellow Fin, Long Tail, Black Fin are warm-water residents. The cold-water species are Big Eye, Albacore and three species of Bluefin. Skipjack is not officially a tuna, yet it's hunted mercilessly for its "light meat," sold in cans by the billions, globally. Warm-water tunas are more primitive than their cold-water brethren. They all possess the same basic body shape, considered the most advanced evolutionary shape for moving efficiently through the water. A pointed front with large eyes flush to the head and near invisible scales offers less resistance enabling water to flow smoothly over its head.

These "sprinters of the sea" are all about speed, which requires copious amounts of oxygen. They rely upon a ramjet breathing system and their own motion passing oxygen-loaded water over the gills. They must move a distance equal to their length every second or they suffocate. To transfer oxygen from the gills to the blood stream, and all other tissues including specialised muscles, the heart of a tuna relative to its body weight is about ten times the size of other fish. Tuna's haemoglobin, a pigment that transports oxygen in blood, is almost equivalent to that of humans. Higher oxygen gives tunas stamina enabling them to undertake trans-Atlantic and Pacific migrations. It also sustains them in their incredibly deep dives. Bluefins move through the water like a sleek torpedo: 46 knots is an average speed with a maximum at 55 knots, only Sailfish have been clocked faster at 59 knots. Do they sleep? This much we know. At night, tunas tend to swim closer together and slower.

There's only one way a 680-kilo (1,500-pound) Bluefin could possibly sustain a metabolic rate requiring consumption of 25 per cent of its body weight daily: to become warm-blooded. It's an exceptional feat, they do it so perfectly that the design of refrigerators mimics their countercurrent heat exchange system. Bluefins have large white muscles extending onto the mass on the flanks with smaller bands or red muscles running the entire length of the animal. Red muscles are located within the white muscles allowing heat from continuously activated white muscles to be retained in the core of the fish. This enables Bluefin to be 14C (25F) warmer than surrounding water. Veins and arteries are bunched together. Warm-blooded veins run alongside the cold, oxygen-rich arterial blood coming through the gills. Heat is effectively passed from the veins to adjacent arteries and returned to the warm muscles. Bluefins are able to raise the temperature of their brain by 6C (11F) above surrounding waters and elevate it by 9C (16F) around its eyes. This astonishing beast is warm-blooded in cold water because it's a competitive advantage over its prey enabling supreme speed. They require mega amounts of food.

Bluefins mature around eight and can live about 30 years. When they get excited they flash neon stripes of blue, green and even purple, which occur during mating or extreme stress e.g. being hooked. Incidentally, chromatophores or coloured cells are controlled by the central nervous system, which change the colour during excitation. Squid and octopuses possess chromatophores that change colour even more dramatically than fish.

Female Bluefins release millions of eggs fertilised by male sperms. We know the spawning grounds of Western Atlantic Bluefin in the Gulf of Mexico and Eastern Atlantic Bluefin in the Mediterranean, Straits of Gibraltar (around Balearic Islands), Sicily, Gulf of Sidra (Libya), Eastern Mediterranean around Turkey and Cyprus, Southern Bluefin along northwestern Australian coastline and eastern tropical Indian Ocean. Spawning lasts one month a year in waters at 24-26C (75-79F). A Bluefin tuna has a one in 40 million chance of reaching adulthood, before humans arrived. They eat almost anything including plastic and they are showing us that pollution from the Fukushima nuclear power plant is circulating in the Pacific Ocean. On 28 May 2012, Pacific Bluefins were found with levels of radioactive caesium ten times higher than the amount measured in tuna off southern California's coast in the previous year. This fact infers that tens of thousands of tonnes of contaminated water, which poured into the North Pacific from the Fukushima plant on 11 March 2011, were far more toxic than previously reported.

The earliest progenitor of sharks dates back to around 400 million years ago. Have you ever wondered what the greatest scavenger in the sea, a two-tonne (2.2-ton) Great White shark, encounters in the Indian Ocean as it travels from Western Australia to eastern South Africa, a distance of over 11,000 kilometres (6,835 miles)? Sharks are amazing disease-free creatures that are on the brink of extinction from a shameless predator: *Homo sapiens*. Apex predators, like some shark species, keep ecosystems in balance. They cull the old and weak, ensuring a high level of fitness amongst their prey. Humans are knowingly exhausting the oceans and as a result jellyfish populations are exploding, and new diseases are emerging.

Sharks inhabit all marine ecosystems from the kaleidoscope-coloured tropical surface waters to the inky, icy depths of the polar seas. They thrive near, or, on coral reefs, mangroves, and rocky shorelines, estuaries and throughout the vast open oceans, worldwide. They have no bones, instead sharks are comprised of cartilage. The counter-shaded grey and white Great White shark is an exceptional predator. Bull sharks leave tropical seas, patrolling fresh water rivers inland as far as 160 kilometres (99 miles) from saltwater. Greenland Sleeper sharks can live for over 200 years, surviving in the Arctic Ocean along the seabed as permanent members of the ecosystem with Greenland Halibut, Belugas and the iconic spiral-toothed male Narwhal whales. Female Lemon sharks return home to give birth in their birthplace of the Bahamas after 15 years at scavenging seas. Mako sharks can travel as fast as 27 knots.

Sharkskin repels water so perfectly it inspired Speedo International to create Fastskin FSII swimsuits. Sharkskin has millions of tiny teeth-like ridges or dermal denticles, which significantly reduce drag and turbulence enabling water to flow effortlessly over the shark's body. Olympians shatter records when they wear these sharkskin-suits in the pool i.e. in Sydney in 2000, 28 of 33 Olympic Gold Medalists donned these suits. Furthermore, the shape of sharks inspired the hull of submarines and torpedoes: a wide middle that tapers at both ends maximizing energy use while at the same time minimising the resistance. While sharks have inspired some companies, others are more socially responsible by protecting them and other creatures as Watson told me: "Lush Corporation is helping us to fight shark finners, sealers and whalers. There are companies that care although most do not. I try to search out the companies that care and I choose to do my business with them."

Open ocean hunting sharks depend entirely upon their forward motion to provide ramjet water flowing over their gills. Some bottom dwelling sharks, on the other hand, are not continuously swimming, relying upon adaptations like breathing in through an extra hole just behind each eye known as a spiracle, they breathe out through the gill slits. Other bottom dwellers like Port Jackson sharks pump water in through the first pair of gill slits and push it out over the remaining four pairs. And the gentle, slow-moving Basking shark, the second biggest fish, filters 1,000 tonnes (1,102 tons) of seawater every hour for air and tiny plankton. Once Basking sharks numbered in the tens of thousands along the North American Pacific coastline but due to the "War Against Nature" they are very rare. In 2011, colleagues in La Jolla, California, outfitted two Basking sharks with satellite-based tracking devices: One fell off but the other one cruised at 3 knots for 4,000 kilometres (2,485 miles), traveling to Hawaii where during the day it fed at 500 metres (1,640 feet) and by night it migrated upward to a depth of 200 metres (656 feet) to continue feeding.

Other complex creatures of the sea have also mastered becoming warm-blooded including Great Whites, Short Fin Makos, Porbeagles, Threshers and Salmon sharks. Parts of their bodies can be 11C (20F) above the ambient water temperatures. Heat is produced by muscle activity and biochemical reactions in their tissues. And heat is conserved by a network of blood vessels, which flow mainly to the swimming muscles, parts of the gut and to the brain. Being warm-blooded in cold water allows these predators a competitive advantage of more speed enabling them to capture more prey. However, it's a costly energy process requiring more food to maintain their warmth.

Ever tasted seawater or wondered how marine creatures contend with sea salts? Sharks deal with it by keeping slightly higher concentrations of salts within their body fluids and tissues than the surrounding seawater. As a result shark's blood has high amounts of urea that osmotically regulates its cells, but it's harmful so they counter it by manufacturing trimethylamine oxide, a protective protein stabiliser. Consequently, sharks produce very small amounts of urine. A 100-kilo (220-pound) shark produces one-tenth the amount of urine compared to the equivalent weight of a human. Sharks don't have swim bladders like most fish instead they depend upon large amounts of squalene oil, rich in hydrocarbons and triterpenes, stored in the liver for buoyancy. Sadly, sharks have been persecuted relentlessly for squalene used in cosmetics, paints, lubricants, candles, leather and tanning.

Speed isn't the only means that some sharks use to capture their prey. They rely upon a couple other finely honed senses like an acute sense of smell, beneath each eye, as nostrils convey continuous information to the olfactory bulb, passing it to large bundles of nerves located in the forebrain. Sharks are ultra sensitive to smelling body fluids of injured or distressed animals as well as blood to a level of one part per million (ppm). They can also detect faint pulses of electricity to as low as 10 millionths of a volt from clusters of tiny pores on the underside of the snout called ampillae of Lorenzini. A shark can sense the breath movements and heart-

beat of a resting fish like Plaice. In
shark uses its large, fabulous, flattene
detector scanning the seafloor for bu
people are intrigued by sharks and that's
shark ecotourism is burgeoning, and wort.   million, annually.

Sharks take a long time to reach sexual maturity, at least
10 years for the Small-Spotted Cat, 15 years for Threshers and 20 years for Dogfish. Long-lived animals, just
like plants, reproduce slowly. The presence of sharks
throughout our oceans is a barometer of its health and
abundance of biodiversity. Sharks are being senselessly destroyed worldwide and the seas are being emptied
and impoverished. Watson rues the loss of sharks: "The
Oceans provide us with almost 80 per cent of the oxygen we breathe. The ocean ecosystem is made up of
food chains that are closely interrelated. Sharks are at
the top of the entire system. They are what scientists
refer to as "keystone species," which means that their
disappearance would cause the entire marine system to
collapse."

My colleague Jeff Hansen, Director of Sea Shepherd
Australia rightfully refers to sharks as "The Doctors of
the Sea" and the Indian Ocean (nor any other ocean)
cannot survive without their vibrant presence. Infuriat-
ingly, the Western Australian government attempted to

tame the eastern Indian Ocean by using baited drum-lines because some misguided bureaucrats believed that if they exterminate all the endangered Great White, threatened Tiger and Bull sharks that come near south-west Western Australia all beachgoers and surfers will be safe. Not only was Western Australia's shark cull incorrect by squandering $20 million, but also the government sanctioned ecocide. A far more prudent fiscal expenditure of taxpayers' dollars would be supporting Australian researchers at Shark Mitigation Systems working on high-tech buoys that could alert lifeguards via satellite to sharks lurking offshore. A prototype has been designed and an operational system could be deployed in 2015. The truth is that any human venturing into a wild ecosystem is at risk. Should all jaguars be massacred in the South American jungles because humans could be killed? Alas, that's a question we won't address because loathsome poachers are driving those phenomenal predators to extinction within a decade or so.

Hansen put it to me this way: "How can we condemn Japan for their indiscriminate killing of whales and dolphins, and do this to our precious protected marine life here in Australia? This baited drumline method is utterly cruel and inhumane, and these animals can take many hours to die." Moreover, baited drumlines attract more sharks because they are tremendous scavengers. Drumlines indiscriminately kill sea turtles and other tour de force sealife. On 12 September 2014, Western Australia's Environmental Protection Agency (EPA) rejected the cruel shark cull. The EPA found a "high degree of scientific uncertainty" surrounding the impact of baited drumlines on the endangered Great White sharks of the Indian Ocean. A passionate Jeff Hansen told me from his office in Perth that, "The EPA should be congratulated for listening to the people, listening to the science and giving sharks and future generations the respect they deserve." One hundred and seventy two magnificent sharks, 3 metres (10 feet) or longer, were brutally massacred between 25 January and 30 April along the coast of southwestern Western Australia. Fourteen sharks, measuring less than 3 metres (10 feet) in length, died on those barbaric drumlines. Four more were euthanised because they were too weak to survive the excruciating pain of being hooked for 9 hours or longer. Stingrays and Mako sharks, both protected species, were also slaughtered as unintended consequences of this ecocide. The EPA received unprecedented interest in saving the sharks with over 7,000 submissions and two petitions with more than 25,000 signatories. Those voices were heard. Indian Ocean sharks are free to roam and scavenge the sea!

Watson kindly shared a lovely poem that he wrote for a very special Tiger shark from the Bahamas named

Emma:

Memoriam for a Special Tiger Shark
By Captain Paul F. Watson

You touched us deep within,
Razor toothed angel soaring beneath cobalted blue
twin hued skies,
Gliding silently, swiftly, effortlessly easy, with formidable fluid
form and fin,
An awesome angelic soul, with smoulderingtiger eyes in
elusive demonic guise.

Tiger Queen of your azure utopian domain,
Ancient perceptions carved from deep, dark dimensions
unknown,
Earthbound aliens enviously denying your proud passion and
pain,
Willfully deaf to every needful cry and mournful moan.
Who are you and what is this?
You taught us to rise above our dangerous frail conceit,
Our unfocused eyes blinded to your mysterious
mirth and bliss,
Most of us seeking and desiring your lethal agonizing defeat.

Emma, we discovered in you a wondrous awesome truth,
You danced with us over the bleached white sands,
We did not recoil in fear from your frightful fin and tooth,
We touched your rigid fins with our pale bold
trembling hands.

Three of our most rare and fair presented themselves to you,
You had the option to connect, to flee, or to kill.
You smiled kindly on their innocent efforts to woo,
Stifling your chilly fear through disciplined force of will.

You had much more to fear from us we know,
We murderous angelic demons in human form,
Your courage was awesome before such a destructive foe,
But you sensed their hearts were unusually gentle
and warm.

The ignorant of us see a stupid and useless fish,
The arrogant of us seek power through your deathly demise
But a few of us possess a more gentle and less
intrusive wish,
We humbly but boldly sought the guidance of one so wise.

In you we saw the strength of the vast ocean,
In you we saw the inter-connectiveness of life,

In you we saw a dazzling spectrum of emotion,
In you we saw a sane solution to senseless strife.

You kissed the angels one by one,
You focused all your thoughts with obsessed desire,
If only communication over the chasm could be won,
Connected by a cosmic rhythmic vibrating wire

You saw that wire vibrate, where we saw nothing at all,
You felt our wish, our desires and our dreams,
We entered your realm and you heard us call,
But others had more nefarious evil schemes.

What you gave us that day will never be forgotten,
You opened up a door of exciting perceptions,
Allowing us to rise above all that is modernly rotten,
The haughty arrogance of human deceptions.

Emma, by our sincere love we betrayed you.
Emma, by our intense desire we slew you,
Emma, by our pathetic ignorance we doomed you,
Forgive us sweet shark, for we know not what we do.

They came in the wake of love and awareness,
Monsters with gaffs and vicious hooks,
Forgive us for being so thoughtless and careless,
In our wake came the pirates and ruthlesscrooks.
They hung you horribly like a gruesome trophy in
ignoble disgrace,
As your hot wild blood dripped upon the sandy beach,
With arrogant smirking smiles upon their ruddy face,
Red necked thieves taking you forever beyond our reach.

They robbed us of a dream that still haunts our sleep,
Emma, you were loved and for you we deeply mourn,
When we think of you, we grow sad and weep,
Diminished forever, is the sea from which you were torn.

We need to break through the hardened barrier of apathy
and hate,
We need to transcend the human centered myth and story,
To wait, may be too late, to salvage us from our
oblivious fate,
We need to restore ourselves, to return to Nature's glory.

Emma may be gone but she spoke with us before she died,

In her eyes we saw her passion, her desire, and her sad
steady sorrow,
She knew her fate, she knew what we would do, and she
softly sighed.
The same thing that we do to her, we will do to ourselves
tomorrow!

The Antarctic krill, driftwood, tunas and sharks are
being pillaged throughout our oceans. So exactly how
much harvesting has taken place in our seas since 1950,
and how much is too much?

How Much is too Much?

Once upon a time, the Grand Banks, off the southeastern Canadian shoreline, were the richest fishing grounds on the globe. In 1497, the explorer, John Cabot, arrived along the Grand Banks and wrote that Cod was, "swarming and so plentiful that they could be scooped into baskets let down (and weighed) with a stone." In 1774, within a couple months, 564 French fishing vessels with 27,500 fishermen took a mother-load valued at $5.5 billion (present US value) of Cod from the Grand Banks. It should, therefore, come as no surprise that by 1992 Cod had vanished from one of the most fecund fisheries ever. Was the Atlantic Cod's crash an indicator of the oceans' health, globally? Technology, human population pressures, greed, duplicity and subsidies have all collided. In this case, the "Perfect Storm" has unimaginable consequences for all life, both marine and terrestrial.

There's a global fishing fleet of four million vessels, 44,000 are industrial factory ships a couple football fields long, employing two per cent of the global fisher-men yet catching over 50 per cent of the edible sealife. In addition, there are over 1.4 billion legal hooks (and perhaps another 250 million illegal hooks) attached to longlines about 90 kilometres (56 miles) in length that, if all connected to one another, would encircle the equator over 522 times, or, the equivalent of 27 return trips to the moon. And in its wake, as much as 25 million tonnes (27.6 million tons) annually of sealife, in fishing jargon called bycatch, are needlessly killed and haphazardly discarded including albatrosses, sea turtles, dolphins and whales. These creatures are accidentally hooked or caught within nets so large that a dozen 747 Boeing jets can easily fit inside the mouth of one net.

Sharks, rays, skates and, my favourite, seahorses are all quickly on the road to extinction. Since 2006, at least 73 million sharks, annually, have been slaughtered, approximately 660 million dead animals. That's enough to fill the Empire State Building with dead shark bodies 18 times, or, one building every 20.3 days, each year! Their numbers are plummeting and they are not being allowed time to reproduce. That means at least 90 per cent of sharks globally have been decimated in all oceans. Poachers are marauding sanctuaries slaughtering sharks in Costa Rica, Columbia, Ecuador and elsewhere. Overt corruption is fueling the annihilation of all shark species. In 2005, Sea Shepherd blew the whistle on the former President of Costa Rica, Abel Pacheco, for receiving $11 million deposited by Taiwan's government into a personal Panamanian bank account. It's not surprising that Watson has been charged by Costa Rica for protecting the sharks after apprehending Taiwanese shark poachers in the Pacific Ocean off the Cocos Island National Park, a crucial Hammerhead, Whitetip Reef and Whale shark mating area. Today, in a world filled with the destruction of nature and rife with corruption, I was not caught off guard in the slightest when Watson revealed: "The Costa Rican judge presiding over the case told me that he would wind things up if I gave him $100,000. I refused, of course."

Since 2006, approximately 1.7 million tonnes (1.9 million tons) of shark flesh have been harvested, annually. In eight years, that's over 15.3 million tonnes (16.9 million tons) of flesh. Exactly what's going on to these grand animals that successfully outlasted the dinosaurs by 65 million years? There's a burgeoning Oriental middle-class with large disposable income creating this gluttonous demand for these abhorrent acts of ecocide.

Millions of sharks are caught, fins and tails sliced off, and then thrown back into the sea. Sharkfins and tails are cartilage with no food value whatsoever, yet they are winding up in Asian soup bowls for an average price of $63 a serving. On the other side of the globe, they sell for even more at $400 a bowl, in cities like Vancouver, London and Miami, where government agencies have turned a blind eye and scientists are either muzzled or indifferent to the devastation happening holus-bolus in the seas. Apparently, sharkfin soup is considered a status symbol, one that was traditionally reserved for either Asian royalty of very high levels of society. Today, sharkfin soup has become the choice as the central dish for middle-class banquet and weddings. Recently, Watson told me: "The Chinese and Hong Kong governments have banned sharkfin soup at state functions and that means they are at least aware of the problem. A recent meeting of Convention of International Trade of Endangered Species finally saw the listing of four species of shark and the exposure of delegates with vested interests that were blocking these listings. There is a worldwide grassroots movement to get sharkfin products banned in cities and states and provinces and this movement is gaining traction. It is a challenge but we must keep pressuring China, Japan, Costa Rica, Spain and other countries involved with the trade in sharkfins to understand that shark populations are being seriously diminished in the world's oceans." Recently, India's Ministry of Environment and Forest, which operates under the authority of the central government of India, brought into effect a "fins naturally attached" policy to prohibit sharkfinning.

At the current frenetic demand and rate of butchery of 73 million stupendous sharks per annum, all 440-shark species and all rays (about 500 species) will be extinct by 2030, or, more likely, sooner. This is absolutely unacceptable and each of us can make a difference. Think about this in the meantime: Nine out of every ten sharks are gone in our oceans. This is the legacy we are leaving our children and these are horrendous crimes against humanity.

The "War Against Nature" has been particularly brutal for tuna. Most of the longlines that perilously crisscross the Pacific, Indian and other oceans ensnare so many other splendid forms of sealife, animals not so dissimilar to you or me, simply endeavouring to make a living, day by day, and survive. Scientists from Duke University, Nicholas School of Environmental & Earth Sciences discovered that longlines in 2003 hooked over 250,000 Loggerhead and 60,000 Leatherback turtles in the Atlantic Ocean. Suffice it to say that the human race will pay an unfathomable price for massacring indiscriminately all sealife.

In January of 2012, one Bluefin tuna sold at auction in Tsukiji Market, Tokyo for a record of $736,000, eclipsing all previous records by hundreds of thousands of dollars. It is exasperating that the economics of this transaction do not truly reflect the health or well-being of the demise of the finest fish to sprint the seas. The Atlantic Bluefin and Pacific Bluefin are doomed. Even worse the Southern Bluefin will go extinct, soon. Already, the Atlantic Bluefin that migrates from the Caribbean, along the eastern US seaboard, is one-tenth the size of the 1960s catches. Making matters even more intractable, China has recently cultivated a palate for Bluefin tuna. An unquenchable affluent market has awoken.

All other tuna species are being unrelentingly hunted. As tuna numbers decline, more and bigger boats are heading for the Pacific Ocean. The latest figures released for 2011 demonstrate that the Pacific tuna catch at more than 2.3 million tonnes (2.5 million tons) was the lowest since 2006. Skipjack stands no chance. How much longer can they withstand this intense and ever-rising technologically advanced fishing fleet?

The demand for Bluefin tuna is so great that now fisherman use light aircrafts to locate younger schools, radioing the exact whereabouts to fishing boats that capture, pen, feed, fatten, slaughter, cold-store and overnight the tuna as air-cargo to Tokyo. It's a process known as "tuna ranching" and it is most assuredly hastening the extinction of Bluefin by many fold. Here's why. First, it began in Australia, then, a decade later, it was introduced into the Mediterranean. Second, since 1996, entire age classes of Southern Bluefin in Australia have been caught, fattened and killed. Bluefins have not been reproducing and Southern Hemisphere populations have been wiped out. Tuna ranchers purchase inexpensive subsidised baitfish and feed them to the penned Bluefins. To add 20 kilograms (44 pounds) of weight during the "fattening stage" it requires 400 kilograms (882 pounds) of baitfish. This crazed form of "ranching" is symptomatic of the current level of subsidised bedlam occurring in the seas. Third, it has attracted detestable poachers, accelerating harvests thus the demise of Eastern Atlantic Bluefin tuna. On 17 June 2010, Malta's inshore fisherman saluted Sea Shepherd for going into Libyan waters and cutting the nets of tuna poachers, freeing close to 800 Bluefin tunas.

What is driving this insatiable demand for Bluefin tuna? It turns out that the Mitsubishi Corporation, the largest global stakeholder in fisheries, is in the process of cornering the world Bluefin tuna market. They already have hundreds of thousands of tons of Bluefin cryoprotected in freezers at minus 60C (minus 76F), and by the end they will have enough to supply the world market for another 15 or possibly 20 years; they will name their price and the unconcerned consumer will pay them. As Watson correctly surmises, "When the Bluefin tuna disappears, they will simply move on to another money-maker. The Oceans are being plundered by companies that don't care about the future of the fishery. Bluefin tuna have no chance of surviving if drastic conservation and the means to enforce restrictions on fishing are not put in place. Many famous chefs are getting involved and refusing to serve Bluefin tuna or swordfish."

Antarctic krill has been heavily fished since the 1970s. Its oil is being used in yet another conspicuous example of unsustainable "fish farming," this time it's occurring on the North American continent. In order to add one kilogram (2.2 pounds) to farmed salmon, farmers must feed them five kilograms (11 pounds) of subsidised fisheries food including krill oil and/or baitfish. Just do the math – sealife currently stands no chance of survival with these flagrant subsidised practices. Although the krill harvest has been lowered significantly since the 1970s, the 2012 limit of 157,000 tonnes (173,062 tons) is still far too high. Given the alacrity of global warming and the missing sea ice in Western Antarctica; the crash of 50 per cent of the Adelie penguins along the northern peninsula of the Shetland Islands where krill fishing boats congregate; and all other seabirds, seals and great whales that depend upon krill as their main food source – it's time to end krill subsidies and moreover shut the entire krill fisheries down. Protecting the integrity of the biodiversity and abundance of krill in the Great Southern Ocean ecosystem is obligatory.

Nine out of the world's ten fisheries are teetering on the edge of collapse. Since the middle of the 19th century, 90 per cent of preindustrial populations of large spawning fish have disappeared. The North Sea has been overfished harder; estimates closer to 96 per cent of commercial fish are gone. Researchers from the University of New Hampshire believe that Haddock, Herring, Mackerel, Yellowtail, Flounder and Winter Flounder have also declined as much as Cod populations. And Cod populations have not rebounded since they crashed in 1992. What's occurring is that as apex predators are removed, humans are "fishing down food webs" as marine biologist Dr Daniel Pauly fittingly termed it. Soon all that will be left is jellyfish and plankton. Japan, incidentally, is already buying over 32,000 kilograms (70,547 pounds) of jellyfish a week, turning it into slender wafers.

Fish biologists Drs Reg Watson and Daniel Pauly of the University of British Columbia discovered that the UN Food and Agriculture Organization (FAO), which had reported global catches yearly since 1950, in fact began to recognise a problem in the 1980s. Yet it took 12 more years for this critical information to become public knowledge. The FAO reported 44 million tonnes (48.5 million tons) of catch in 1950 and by the early 1990s it was 80 million tonnes (88.2 million tons). The total world harvest rose in 2000 to 110 million tonnes

(121.3 million tons) or the equivalent of packing 100.6 Empire State Building's or one building every 3.3 days with dead animals (not including bycatch, poaching or shark slaughter)! What was the reason for the enormous and grossly unsustainable reported numbers? False reporting by China. Since 1988 the actual worldwide decline has been at least 700,000 tonnes (771,617 tons) a year. Essentially, the sea has been emptied of older fish that are of paramount importance for reproduction. For example, Plaice is harvested by the time it reaches 6 years old, yet that can live for up to 40 years. Extreme fishing pressure on Cod and Haddock revealed that both species are now breeding one year earlier – a rare example of human-induced evolution.

So what happens when fisheries near the surface are emptied? The fallacy that technology is the answer has lead humans to begin, not only depleting all deep-sea fisheries, but worse; inflicting irreparable damage to the ocean floor and its salubrious seamounts with ancient corals that once were chocked-full of life. The subsidised destruction of the seafloor is so vast that NASA satellites regularly detect 25 kilometres (16 miles) of devastating sediment clouds blanketing the seas.

In 1969 the Soviets first found the existence of seamounts, northwest of Hawaii. The Japanese fishing fleet joined them and together, with their kilometre-and-a-half (one mile) deep nets, within 8 years wiped-out Armor-heads. In the late 1980s the same scenario of deep-sea plunderous fisheries repeated itself, this time with the long-lived Slimeheads (Orange Roughy). By 2001, Orange Roughy vanished, fisheries liquidated. When I asked Watson about lowering the global catch limits he told me "I wish but as legal catch limits are lowered, illegal takes increase. Every single commercial fishery in the world is in a state of collapse. We have already destroyed numerous fish populations and as we remove one species we move onto another. In the Nineties a fish called an Orange Roughy was in great demand. It was sold everywhere. You don't see it anymore because it has been fished out. Why? Because the Orange Roughly takes 45 years to mature and lives to be 200 years old. We wiped out the breeding numbers leaving only imma-ture fish in small numbers. But never mind, the fishing industry set their sights on the Patagonia and Antarctic Toothfish. The value of a fish maintaining the ecological integrity of the oceans is far greater for us all than on someone's dinner plate."

Bottom trawlers have huge nets with rockhoppers, long metal bars attached to the base of the net's mouth, each bar is one metre (3.3 feet) thick weighing an eighth of a tonne (275 pounds). Rockhoppers can move boulders weighing 25 tonnes (27.5 tons). Metal ticklerchains at-tached to rollers on the net stir-up the deep-sea muddy bottom, creating a calamitous cacophony, spooking fish from their security habitat, resulting in those visible sediment plumes captured from outerspace. North Atlantic bottom trawling has reduced all known bottom-dwelling fish by at least 80 per cent since the 1970s. Rockhoppers ruin seamounts smashing them to smithereens along with thousands-of-years-old deep-sea corals (the slowest growing organisms in the ocean), which now resemble war-torn Middle Eastern combat zones. Rockhoppers and ticklerchains raze deep-sea habitat and sextillion seafloor residences; in a couple centuries some may return, but coldwater deep corals will take many millenniums to recover. I might also remind you that amongst this reckless abandon along the seafloor and seamounts, estimated at twice the size of contiguous United States annually, humans are loosing untold and undiscovered cancer, pain, diabetes and coronary medicines from deep-sea sponges and awe-inspiring cold corals gardens.

The "War Against Nature" has escalated into a prolonged global looting spree; nature is defenseless against the onslaught of advanced equipment such as: Satellite operated fish tracking buoys called "fishing aggregating devices" that dot thousands of square kilometres of oceans. Echo sounders constantly bombard ocean depths, mapping seabeds with 3D images of the floor and with precision where to drop the trawlers, rockhoppers and ticklerchains. Split-beam fish finder sonar devices are as accurate as those deployed by naval submarines, persistently hunting for Haike, which appears as clusters of green dots. Bird radar searches for flocks of seabirds, which gather above schools of fish. Doppler radar incessantly monitors sea temperatures noting where cold upwelling currents occur bringing rich nutrients to phytoplankton, feeding krill, sustaining fisheries like Anchovies and Sardines that are prey for tuna, Marlin and sharks. Fishermen receive daily reports form NOAA showing satellite images and global sea temperatures. And on and on it goes. On top of all that oceans are being viscously poached; in the Southern Ocean Russians, Spanish, Taiwanese, Uruguayan, Namibian, Chinese and others are harvesting huge unrecorded amounts of Patagonian Toothfish (Chilean Seabass) and Antarctic Toothfish (Antarctic Cod). "We have the laws to stop this illegal exploitation but governments do nothing," affirms Watson. In addition, off West Africa in the Atlantic Ocean, the World Wildlife Fund believes that the European Union countries are under-reporting their ocean catches by a factor of eight. Nature and her bounty-rich marine ecosystems, globally, has nil chance of survival against this avarice fleet of 44,000 factory ships working 24/7, 365 days.

In 2012 the worldwide catch was set at a whopping 90 million tonnes (99.2 million tons) or enough to fill 82

Empire State Building's at one building every 4.5 days with dead sealife (and this does not include bycatch or shark poaching)! It's a $240 billion annual global industry in dire straights and according to University of California, Berkeley scientists it is rife with child slavery. Since nine out of ten shallow fisheries have been fully exploited the deepsea fisheries of Lingtusk, Greenland Halibut and Blue Whiting are currently being ransacked. As a result all known commercial deep-sea fish populations have plunged beneath 80 per cent of 1970s levels. Repugnant fishery subsidies of at least of $34 billion per annum have created an obese over-capacity with a global fleet at least 72-fold larger than otherwise feasible, in turn creating pressures on government bureaucracies uninterested and conveniently unaware of the laws of ecology, but quick to increase subsidies whilst all fisheries are collapsing. Moreover, special interest groups are driving this global oceanic ecocide with loathsome swarms of self-aggrandising lobbyists, flaunting alligator shoes and snake-skinned attaché cases demanding and receiving blatantly unsustainable fisheries quotas. Obviously, it's time to terminate all fisheries subsidies, including fossil fuel subsidies, and protect the remaining integrity of the debilitated oceans for human survival in the forthcoming decade.

"I coined a word to describe the reason that politicians do nothing to curb the excesses of the fishing industry.

"Homopechephobia" or the "fear of fishermen." The fishing industry has become one of the biggest welfare recipients on the planet. Billions of dollars in subsidies allow the fishing boats to continue to plunder the seas. The fishing industry cannot survive without subsidies. The problem is that there is a lack of political and economic will to conserve life in the sea and there is incredible incentive, thanks to subsidies and demand to destroy life in the seas. We need politicians with the courage to say no more welfare to the fishing industry bums," says Watson with a sound understanding of exactly what's going on with fisheries pilfering all the oceans.

Currently, about 30 million tonnes (33 million tons) or a third of the global catch ends up as fish meal or fish oil, which as we've seen is utterly unsustainable. Watson cites another good example of how up-side-down the subsidised fisheries have become: "Domestic cats eat more tuna than do all the seals in the world combined; 2.5 million tonnes (2.75 million tons) of fish are fed to domesticated cats every year and, when you think about it, it is a strange situation because if a cat were to encounter a tuna in nature, the tuna would eat the cat."

One thing is for sure "decreasing deep-sea biodiversity has an impact on everything else, it reduces our chance of survival even further and makes a future for 'us' on this Earth unlikely," says a candid Watson. Ocean habitat destruction and the present industrial fishing armada are on a tear the likes of which has never occurred since our blue planet began life 3.5 billion years ago. And Watson "thinks it will take nothing short of a catastrophe, worldwide to change our relationship to the planet." Already, a team of scientists lead by Dr Boris Worm of Dalhousie University concluded that at the present annual rate of decimating sealife: 122 Empire State Building's packed with dead animals – the oceans will become lifeless is less than three and a half decades.

I agree whole-heartedly with Watson's prediction, "The one sure thing is that we do not have much time." As we will see later, there's an ace in the hole, allowing nature and the sea respite if humans choose, wisely. For the meantime let us regroup, clear our minds and begin to examine the beauty and excellence of two extraordinary forms of spellbinding sealife: The first glides through the sea whilst the second floats over top of it. The wonders of the sea are adrenalising, in fact; they are the finest masterpieces on our blue planet.

Ancient but Not Primitive

Before humans sea turtles swam the sea for hundreds of millions of years. They represent a heavenly strand of life lost in a time warp that saw all other dinosaurs vanish. Having evolved on land 200 million years ago these beauties now spend their entire lives at sea except to lay eggs on rugged beaches around the globe. They are ancient but not primitive.

There are seven species that paddle Earth's oceans, in ascending size they are: Kemp's Ridley, Olive Ridley, Hawksbill, Flatback, Loggerhead, Green, and the regal Leatherback. Leatherbacks are Earth's last remaining warm-blooded reptile. A female can very easily reach 375 kilograms (827 pounds) and weigh far in excess of a half a tonne (1,102 pounds). They outlasted their only natural predator Tyrannosaurus–Rex by 65 million years. Since the 1980s humans have eradicated Leatherbacks and all other sea turtle populations by at least 95 per cent.

Even the smallest sea turtle Kemp's is large at 40 kilograms (88 pounds). Greens and Loggerheads are about 185 kilograms (408 pounds), and Leatherbacks are the record-holders at up to five times larger than Loggerheads. All sea turtles have skin similar in structure to that of sharks, adapted to shed friction with dermal denticles: They are streamlined extraordinaire. All sea turtles except Leatherbacks have shells. Instead their hard-bone carapace is louvered with scaly scutes, forming an intricate jigsaw comprised of thousands of tiny bones covering a rich-oily-fat with durable fibrous tissue. The belly is made up of a thin, narrow oval bone reinforced with heavy fibrous, thick tapered tissue. Leatherbacks shape looks like that of a barrel compared to the other six species. Sea turtles possess upper jaws with two fang-like teeth, while the lower jaw has but one very large and extremely sharp lower canine. Their rear flippers are highly dexterous likened in sensitivity to an elephant's trunk. A female uses rear flippers to meticulously dig a one metre-deep (3.3 feet-deep) cylindrical chamber for her eggs.

Leatherbacks are the fastest-growing and heaviest reptile in the sea. A Leatherback hatchling will grow 30 times its size and add 6,000 fold in weight. They generally mature by the age of 12 and live in the wild for about six decades. They are also the fastest swimming sea turtle with the widest distribution and migration of any reptile. Only some of the great whales exceed those migratory distance. And only three toothed whales: Sperms, Cuvier's Beaked and Narwhals surpass Leatherbacks deep-diving prowess.

Humans are the only creatures to pose a lethal threat to sea turtles in over 200 million years of their illustrious history on Earth. Poachers have callously taken sea turtle eggs, murdered these superb swimmers for their meat and oil, and continue to unscrupulously supply the frenzied Asian demand for aphrodisiac powders. Until outlawed in 1992, driftnets drowned tens of millions of sea turtles and thousands of abandoned driftnets known as "ghost nets" still continue to lay waste to thousands more each year. All throughout the 1980s Watson and Sea Shepherd scoured the high seas for driftnets, cutting hundreds apart, freeing sea turtles, dolphins, whales, sharks, tuna and all other trapped sealife. Watson says, "You can smell those walls of death many miles before you can see them." Freeing captured marine life on a regular basis certainly hasn't ingratiated him in any countries' good books, but with a grin more reminiscent of a child on Christmas Eve he'll tell you that, "Nothing I do is done to please people; I work exclusively for the oceans!"

Watson spent a good chunk of the 1990s searching for ghost nets to free Leatherbacks and Loggerheads and stopping poachers. There were about 90,000 Leatherbacks in the Pacific in the 1990s -- today there are less than 5,000 remaining. The Atlantic populations are in a bit better shape and some have even increased due to tremendous conservation initiatives and public education. There are not many endangered Loggerheads left either in the seas. Watson holds them particularly dear to his heart because as he fondly explained to me, "In 1979 when I was searching for the pirate whaler *Sierra* in the North Atlantic I was two days out of the Azores heading towards Portugal when I saw a large migration of Loggerhead turtles. I stopped the ship and we spent six hours swimming with the turtles and then carried on. The next day at noon I spotted a ship one hundred and eighty miles off the Portuguese coast. It was heading South and we were heading East. It was the *Sierra,* the very ship I was looking for. If not for the turtles stopping us for six hours we would have never have found the *Sierra* at all. The turtles led us to this savage killer of whales. We rammed her twice and ended her grisly and ignoble career."

Sea turtles' four legs are wings in the sea, and shovels on the beach. I was blessed in the late 1990s to witness a female Leatherback come ashore along Baja California, Mexico and carefully excavate a body pit for her eggs. Standing next to her huge back at well over a metre (3.3 feet) high, she seemed to take little notice of me. I stood motionless in awe with utter reverence of this colossal creature. She laid about five and half dozen billiard ball-sized eggs. The first couple dozen eggs are yokeless, creating air space, stabilising humidity, protecting against fungus or insects and after a month of incubation provide elbowroom for the unusually long-winged hatchlings.

Each Leatherback averages seven nests in a breeding season about ten days apart. Females lay between 65 to 85 eggs in the Pacific and Atlantic populations, respectively. Between 450 and 600 eggs are produced in a year; that's more than any other reptile or mammal. It takes a large amount of energy to lay eggs every two weeks. The yokes alone are expensive on the female body, as she must draw heavily upon her reserves. The reason why they wait four years between laying such large clutches is to build up their reserves again. "If your nests are subjected to tropical storms, flooding, and washouts then evolution leads to these creatures laying a lot of eggs," says marine biologist Dr Carl Safina. Leatherbacks prefer rugged steep shorelines with open faces and coarse sandy beaches. The trade-off is that they loose some of those nests; it offers the new borne hatchlings a chance to bee-line to the ocean usually under the cover of darkness, before predators like vultures and hawks engulf them. Similar to salmon, sea turtles breed and lay eggs at the sites where they were born. Beaches unfortunately change over decades and human development with lights has imposed no end of problems for hatchlings that instead of heading toward the ocean often wind up going in the wrong direction. Lights also discourage females from coming onto beaches. The hatchlings use a cue of brightness of a star-lit sky and moonbeams reflecting across the ocean to lead them away from the dark jungle behind. The darker the beach and shore the more star-lit contrast the sky. Thankfully, along the Atlantic Florida coastline there's no outdoor lighting allowed from June to October in 20 counties and 46 municipalities. Lights are shut-off covering 95 per cent of Florida's Loggerhead and Green turtle nesting sites.

As soon as Leatherbacks over-sized flippers touch the surf they instinctively start swimming and diving seaward. They also immediately orient themselves with Earth's magnetic field swimming far offshore away from coastal birds and predatory fish. Quickly their paddling smoothens almost appearing effortlessly. They rest part of the night and then continue swimming. When resting they tuck their flippers along their side, far less detectable appearing in the Atlantic like a small mass of Sargassu seaweed. In fact, they search for opulent mats of seaweeds and phytoplankton in both oceans, which provides ever-important security cover for young hatchlings. Amongst the leafy cover are tiny larval crabs, shrimps, small jellyfish, snails, salps, fish eggs, barnacles, crabs, seahorses, young octopuses, edible vegetation and ocean striders -- a delectable array of foods for the quickly growing Leatherback hatchlings.

In the Atlantic the hatchlings ride the Gulf Stream Current which hugs the Floridian coastline traveling north until they reach Cape Hatteras, North Carolina taking them directly east through the Saragossa Sea (the only sea without land on any of its boundaries) until reaching the Azores of Portugal, there they drift past the Canaries and Cape Verde Islands into West Africa. They return to North America some years later or more likely after a decade or so. Very little is known about the first couple years of Leatherbacks. When they re-appear onto the radar screen they're three quarters of a metre (2.5 feet) long and many are entangled in either fishing nets or deadly longlines at a rate of one turtle per 1,000 hooks. About one in every four or five Atlantic Leatherbacks studied have line scars from fishery gear. As Leatherbacks grow larger they move back onto continental shelves and begin foraging the seafloor and seagrasses feeding upon crabs and a wide variety of shellfish. Leatherbacks constantly wander in search of foods.

Sea turtles, albatrosses and other seabirds have adapted to sea salts by using glands near their eyes to filter and expel these septic salts; these marine masters are able to drink full-strength seawater without dehydrating. Salt-water fish and other marine mammals including whales, on the other hand, rely upon their kidneys to detoxify salinity.

We have so much to learn from these breathtaking beauties. Sophisticated satellite trackers with dedicated marine biologists, usually working with shoestring budgets, have uncovered some of their incredible life histories. It wasn't until the 1970s they discovered sea turtles migrated. Up until the mid 1980s it was conjecture that Caribbean Leatherbacks ventured as far north as the frigid waters off the Grand Banks. Then in the 1990s they revealed that Loggerhead juveniles from Mexico undertook an epic swim of almost 10,000 kilometres (6,214 miles) to the shores of Japan where some years later they breed. All species of sea turtles take a long time to reach their reproductive age. This much we do know, in warmer waters, breeding begins when they get to between 20 and 25 years old; whilst in cooler waters, the process of maturity takes about a decade longer after sea turtles reach midway into their third decade of life.

Climate disruption is wreaking havoc with sea turtles; it's destroying nesting sites, increasing seawater temperatures by 0.8C (1.4F), and causing Floridian sea turtles to nest 10 days earlier. If the sand gets hotter or turtles nest earlier and sands remain marginally cooler this directly affects male/female hatchling ratios. One ancient trait that sea turtles still retain is undifferentiated sex chromosomes; instead, sex is environmentally determined by temperature during the middle one third of incubation. Warmer temperatures produce females. Already Florida's Loggerheads produce between 90 and 100 per cent females. Southern Carolina and Georgia's Loggerheads are over 60 per cent females so if something goes wrong with the northern population, like worsening affects of global warming, the entire coastal Loggerhead population is at risk to loosing its males, and therefore its facing extinction.

Each of the seven sea turtles depends upon different marine species within the food chain to reach their respective sizes, which range from large to enormous. Green's graze upon seagrasses, Loggerheads crunch crabs, Ridley's chow crabs, shellfish, barnacles, fish eggs, snails, worms, salps and sea squirts. Flatbacks forage for sea pens, other soft corals, sea cucumbers; Hawksbill's specialise on sponges laced with toxins filled with lattices of glass spicules; and Leatherback's predilection: Venomous hot-stinging jellyfish – they suck them in, close their mouth and snort two powerful jets of water out their nostrils. Leatherbacks forage day and night requiring huge amounts of food. Young Leatherbacks will eat their body weight, daily. Leatherback's esophagus runs their entire length of their body and loops back again into the stomach. It's lined with spikes specifically for sucking-in vast numbers of jellies.

In order to exceed half-a-tonne (1,102 pounds) Leatherbacks have some truly amazing adaptations enabling them to swallow Lion's Mane and Moon jellies living in freezing Northern Hemisphere waters. Leatherbacks could only undertake migrations that span thousands of kilometres if their bodies were enormous. Large bodies store energy, effectively allowing these beauties to travel long distances between feeding zones. Bigger, rounder Leatherback bodies conserve heat from bones tipped with thick cartilage, crammed with blood vessels delivering plenty of nutrients, a trait common amongst mammals.

From the tropics to the Arctic Circle Leatherbacks maintain a body temperature of between 25-29C (77-84F) even in polar waters at 5C (41F). They take advantage of their size to both conserve and generate heat using a circulation system made up of heat-generating tissues, effective digestion and movement of muscles to generate body warmth. As a result their metabolic rates are three times higher than normal reptiles. Two kinds of fat layers both conserve and generate heat. An outer white fat is insulative like that of mammalian blubber whilst a brown layer of fat is loaded with blood vessels that generate heat. No other reptile has brown fat;

rather it's a more common feature amongst mammals and some birds. Leatherback's circulating system can either flow blood toward or away from skin for heating or cooling it.

A counter-current heat exchange system maintains the warmth of flippers despite icy polar-water temperatures. Flippers are laden with bundles of 70 veins and 20 arteries returning heat that disperses the cold into Leatherback's core for immediate arterial warmth. Their muscles possess phenomenal chemical resistance to cold temperatures. Cell metabolic rates remain constant regardless of temperatures ranging from 5 to 38C (41 to 100F). This unique response to muscular performance has inspired medical researchers seeking cures for human degenerative muscular diseases e.g. muscular dystrophy.

Caribbean Leatherbacks migrate 5,000 kilometres (3,107 miles) on their journey to the Grand Banks continental shelf jammed full of jellies at a density of one meal per square metre (11 feet^2). They gorge on Lion's Mane with a bell as wide as a big garbage can lid (two metres wide or 6.6 feet) and tentacles as long as 75 metres (246 feet), planet Earth's longest true jellies. These jellies live for months before spawning and dying. Exactly how do Leatherbacks locate jellies under poorly lit daytime conditions at depths exceeding 50 metres (164 feet) or during the night? Nobody knows. Do they smell or hear them? Another unknown.

This much we do know: in late spring Leatherbacks from the south appear in the frigid northeastern waters. They follow the Laurentian Channel, which intersects the continental shelf. There's one spot in Cabot Strait where the subsea geography provides the most optimal conditions on the globe for Lion's and Moon jellies, and that's exactly where the highest densities of Leatherbacks congregate. By late summer it's teaming with these jumbo sea turtles, no fishing gear or traps to tangle them – as these waters have been well and truly fished-out; Cod stocks have not retuned since the 1992 crash.

In order to find jellies and other forage, sea turtles developed two primo systems for storing and using oxygen during extended dives. Sea turtles have a backup system in the event that oxygen runs out. In just one breath a sea turtle can exchange more than 80 per cent of its breath (humans can only achieve a 10 per cent mark). With a few quick breaths of two or three seconds a sea turtle can completely refill and refuel its body. When a sea turtle holds its breath; it's able to extract oxygen from every cell in its lungs to near undetectable oxygen levels.

Sea turtles dive during the night and day spending greater than 95 per cent under water. Leatherbacks, on the other hand, spend 20 to 45 per cent at the surface; dives vary from a couple minutes for migrating to a-half-an-hour foraging. But they can stay under water for an hour or longer. Kemp's can dive easily to 30 metres (98 feet); Hawksbill's to 100 metres (328 feet); Green's 125 metres (410 feet); Flatback's 155 metres (509 feet); Loggerhead's 250 metres (820 feet); Olive Ridley's 300 metres (984), and Leatherbacks to at least as deep as 1.4 kilometres (4,593 feet) or 140 atmospheres of bone crushing pressure and numbing cold conditions in total darkness. Below 100 metres (328 feet), sea turtles collapse their lungs, very likely accounting for why Leatherbacks have such flexible, jigsaw pieces which make up their outer shell-like surface, it's resistant to cracking during the deepest dives. Air is displaced into both its cartilage and reinforced trachea, precluding painful poisoning from nitrogen seeping into the blood stream (known to divers as "the bends"). Leatherbacks pre-dissolve oxygen reserves directly into their red blood cells (the highest of any reptile); it's a system that takes more oxygen than their lungs. When a Leatherback dives its heart rate drops by one third, staying at one beat per minute until it surfaces. Their heart is much larger comparatively than all other sea turtles. It's a stunning evolutionary adaptation, which passes blood through the heart wall from one chamber to the next, pooling it away from the lungs. Upon surfacing, before the shunting port on the heart closes, it sends recycled blood to enrich the lungs as they re-inflate.

Some Leatherbacks can travel 125 kilometres (78 miles) in a day but more normally it's between 30 and 50 kilometres (18 and 31 miles). Northern forages for Lion's and Moon jellies take on average 12-minute swallow dives. When they migrate, dives last about a-half-an-hour but just a metre (3.3 feet) below the surface. When Leatherbacks reach warmer southern (Northern Hemisphere) waters they regularly dive to 500 metres (1,640 feet).

Lovemaking is a rather rough and tumble affair in the world of sea turtles. Males converge near female nesting grounds, chasing, grabbing and biting, attempting to hook on with more curved claws on the front flipper (Leatherbacks are clawless). Some female' resist, while other males chase a would-be couple, dislodging the male and attempting to mate. Females are receptive about one month before egg-laying. If the female is receptive, the male curls his long tail under the shell and an erect penis ejaculates sperm into her cloaca. They embrace for hours – a charming sight to behold. Females store sperm until ovulation. Both males and females are polygamous.

Leatherbacks nesting on New Guinean beaches go through some of the heaviest longlined-hooked waters on the globe between Indonesia and the Philippines. After nesting, Pacific Leatherbacks swim east to North America crossing an enormous mine-field of several thousand kilometres fraught with deadly hooks set for tuna along the central equatorial Pacific. Duke University scientists estimated in the Pacific Ocean that 4,000 Loggerheads and 1,000 Leatherbacks die a gruesome and painful death each year from those longlines. Those longliners also hook and kill mammals like Short-Finned Pilot whales, Blainville's Beaked whales, the False Killer whales, Humpback and Sperm whales, Risso's-, Bottlenose-, Spotted-, Common- and Spinner-dolphins. Those dreadful monofilament lines with billions of hooks drifting throughout our oceans are senselessly eradicating all marine life.

Once upon a time there were a billion living sea turtles gracing the oceans then 600 years ago the "War Against Nature" began expunging them. Today every species is well below five percent of their original numbers, with less than 5,000 Pacific Leatherbacks left; they are damned. What I enjoy so much about children and my students is their curiosity and thirst to understand the function of each organism. For instance, I'm often asked what role do the sea turtles play in the ocean? Before the "War Against Nature" seagrasses were kept well grazed by Green's, today seagrasses or what's left of them are overgrown, and riddled with diseases. Caribbean sponges called *Londrilla nucula* are smothering the reefs or what's left of them in Belize, when healthy populations of Hawksbill's lived they consumed those sponges, keeping populations in-check. The waters are now coursing with jellyfish and so few Leatherbacks. Without the sea turtles, the oceans, coral reefs, cold coral gardens and seagrasses are all collapsing.

The balance of Earth's marine ecosystems has been horribly disrupted and global warming with its rising sea levels have been delivering pummeling surfs to beaches, damaging prime Leatherback nesting sites, which were once pristine, safe and secluded. From Australia's Gold Coast to Mexico's Baja and the Caribbean's Trinidad all beaches have suffered extensive erosion during the past decade. If humans continue to murder them, poach their eggs and deploy more fishing gear there will be no more sea turtles. As we will see shortly plastics are delivering the coup de grâce to these admirable creatures. We know if humans can stop killing sea turtles that conservation efforts by people to rebuild populations are working in the Atlantic, and some species are responding.

Reckless human over-exploitation is now genetically detectable in the sea turtles. Australian researchers used DNA samples from 334 turtles collected across 18 nesting sites along 2,897 kilometres (1,800 miles) of Mexico's Pacific coast. They found that between 1960 and 1990, more than 2 million Olive Ridley turtles, 350,000 in 1968 alone, and their eggs were commercially harvested along the coast of Mexico. Intense over-harvesting of a few nesting sites caused a significantly measurable reduction in genetic diversity in Olive Ridley turtles along the entire coastal Mexican region. In addition, they discovered that harvesting of individuals and nests has led to a direct behavioural change whereby nesting females no longer nest in synchronised and massive mode with other females; instead, Olive Ridley's now seek a solitary nest site.

Lastly, turtle poaching has reached a new demented level. On 31 May 2013, Costa Rican turtle conservationist Jairo Mora Sandoval was kidnapped, beaten, and shot in the head by turtle poachers armed with AK-47 rifles. "The shark poachers and the turtle poachers are a law onto themselves in Costa Rica and the government does nothing because there is a demand for both shark fins and turtle eggs in China and Costa Rica does what China and Japan tell them to do. On top of that, drug lords are now offering weapons and drugs to the poachers, instructing them to keep conservationists off the beaches. This way the drug traffickers are not being hindered. The drug cartels are becoming more influential in Costa Rica and they are more and more using fishermen (to bring them cheap fuel and smuggle drugs in shark bodies) and poachers (replacing the turtle eggs with drugs) to help their illegal activities," says Watson who has personally offered $30,000 for the arrest and conviction of Mora Sandoval's assassins. Sea Shepherd UK recently acquired a new addition to their fleet and named the vessel *Jairo Mora Sandoval* in honour of the late 26-year-old conservationist.

Before we examine nature's truest gliders please take solace from Dr Carl Safina's compassionate counsel: "Do all you can, don't worry about the odds against you. Wield the miracle of life's energy, never worrying whether we may fail, concerned only that whether we fail or succeed we do so with all our might. That's all we need to know to feel certain that all our force of diligent effort is worth our while on Earth."

Blood Hounds of the Sea

Albatross are the greatest long distance wanders on Earth, traveling to the limits of seemingly limitless seas. Their bodies evolved to glide, indefinitely. These beauties float through the air rather than fly, at high speeds. They are a symbol of good luck and truly a beneficial companion for those who have spent any time at sea.

A Wandering albatross's heart actually beats slower during flight than while sitting on the sea. Black-brown albatross use about the same energy while flying compared to brooding a chick on their nest. The Gray albatross at sea has the lowest cost of flight ever recorded. It turns out their wings lock at the shoulder as well as locking at the elbow for incredible rigidity, likened to the unfolded position of a switchblade.

Before maturing, an albatross stays at sea for years. They spend an astounding 95 per cent of their lives at sea, most of it flying. They come to land only to breed on the remotest islands hundreds or thousands of kilometres from continents. An albatross covers the equivalent distance of flying around Earth's equator at least three times every year (120,225 kilometres or 74,704 miles)). In fact, a 50-year-old albatross has flown at least 5.9 million kilometers (3.7 million miles).

Air sacs surround all their organs and extend into their hollow wing bones. Skeletons make up only 13 per cent of their body weight, while flight muscles account for a modest 9 per cent of weight. For Royal and Wandering albatross, their flight muscles diminish to a meager six per cent. These creatures are pure gliders – extreme range beasts. Wingspan to width of Wandering albatross is 18 to 1 comparable to the best human made glider. Lift to drag, or the lifting force to air resistance is an incredible 40 to 1. Triple that of most eagles. Albatross are incapable of sustained flapping during flight, instead they are entirely dependent on continuous winds, so they admirably evolved in the windiest place on Earth: The Great Southern Ocean.

Superlative and extreme in size, duration and endurance; albatross are Olympians of the air. Even the smallest species has a two-metre (6.6-foot) wingspan. Wandering and Royal's possess the longest wings in nature, over 3.4 metres (11.2 feet) from tip to tip. Wandering weigh 12 kilograms (26 pounds), twice that of a bald eagle. The oldest albatross to date, a Royal, was living well into its 60s. They may be able to live for a century. Scientists haven't had the privilege of studying them long enough to know.

Humans have affected albatross adversely. Fisheries and global warming are devastating them. The fate of the albatross is inextricably linked to human activities in the sea including suffocating them with plastic. It's something Watson has observed worsening dramatically over the past 40 years: "We have to understand that it's a question of making a real commitment. Our ultimate goal is to ensure that the continuum of life on this planet can be maintained. Most people do not think very much about the future because we are trapped in a media culture that is defining our own reality." That said, I think the longer Watson sticks to his dangerous work the better the chance ordinary people around the globe will raise their consciousness. His television show, "Whale Wars," is helping to achieve that noble goal.

Anyone who has spent any amount of time on remote islands, where these majestic creatures breed, are deeply touched by these glorious gliders. In 1912, the renowned ornithologist Robert Cunningham Murphy visited a sub-Antarctic island, observed a Wandering albatross and wrote that it touched him so profoundly, a truly spiritual experience, "I feel like I've been to church." Others have experienced sublime serenity like ornithologist, Dr Frank Gill, who recounted a day watching nesting Wanderers: "There was such wisdom on those beautiful eyes that had seen so many years. In all my lifetime experiences with birds, no moment was so moving." When I asked Watson about his special encounter with an albatross he warmly smiled, "Once off the coast of New Zealand, an albatross was following my ship the *Steve Irwin*. It kept coming closer to where I was standing on the bridge wing of the ship. I put out my arm and the albatross glided towards me, passing so close that the tip of his wing touched my fingers. They are incredible birds." Watson shared with me his touching albatross encounter, a poem written for his then girlfriend, a Maori singer in Aotearoa.

Toroa Raukura

By Captain Paul F. Watson

Whakarongo
Wkakarongo mai taku hine
Whakarongo O te K? k? p?
Taku Toroa raukura
Korowhitawhita e
Ruia r? te rongopai
Ikei runga Taku moana ? io.

Riding the winds focused on devotion
Spirit of grace teasing the angry waves
The wind caressed with erotic motion
Gliding swiftly over dead sailor's graves

The bird flew out of the fog from the North
And towards my ship's station it did fly
Upon the quarterdeck my hand reached forth
This pale solo Seraph was hardly shy.

Reaching forth, I touched the feathered wing tip
Blue eyes peered piercingly into my own.
Speaking the voice of Rangi to my ship

Toroa's heart shivered in a doleful moan

Upon the shore a Maori princess stands
Hearing the cry of Toroa from afar
Tangaroa painfully screams across the lands
Light falls upon her from a distant star.

Surf savagely kissing the corralled shore,
Waters relentlessly pounding the stone
Winning back the stolen land its endless chore
Are we separate and are we alone?

Spirits connecting through feathered magic
Passing Lani Kahuna's ancient grave
What the Albatross has seen is tragic
To this despair I shall not be a slave

I am k?pene, kairoro, a man.
Kaiwhakatangi Maori are you,
Pirinitete weaver wondrously grand
Chances for happiness so frail and few

Feel the heartbeat of the land and the sea,

Kia tika te marama, and so bright,
From the deep sea Toroa calls to me,
That hallowed bird is a marvelous sight.

My anchor chain fetters my heart and soul,
You are quite soundly bound by strings and chords
Conflict turning the heart as black as coal
Our quick tongues hammered into deadly swords

Unraveling the mystery is a task
Beneath the enigma there lies a mask
Answers to all questions we dare not ask
Answers held by Tane in the grass.

The feather parts the mists of time's still breath,
Deep desire gives birth to daring dreams
Despair gives birth to destruction and death
Delirium foils the devils schemes.

We are ships sailing on the sea of life
Do we cross safe or crash upon the rocks?
Must we endure the conflict and the strife?
Mistakes are made, no turning back the clocks.

We can make port no matter the weather
Our voices joined over the land and sea.
Joined by the beauty of a feather
Toroa calling me to you - you to me.

I do not know what the future does hold
Joyous life or dark death it matters not,
My fear is that the future will be cold
My hope is that it will be warm and hot

There is ancient alchemy here somewhere
Oceans within oceans, above, below.
Winged feathered messengers so true and fair
The albatross for hope, for death the crow.

With Toroa, to the wind, my heart I fling,
Upon the stormy wind I hear you sing
Words in harmony dance along the wing
Sometimes the words caress, sometimes they sting

To earn your sweet kiss, I endure the sting
Rare treasures are not won without a fight
Into my hand Toroa has dropped a ring

A ring of white feathers, delicate and light.

Hau ki tua – breath from beyond moana
Fill my strong sails and navigate my heart
Steer me to fair Aotearoa's koanga
He k? angiangi smiles upon my chart.

In my quest I follow the Albatross.

By attaching small, highly sophisticated satellite track-ing probes to whales, sharks, sea turtles, giant fish like tunas, seals and albatross scientists are beginning to get a "big picture" view of where these dazzling oceanic dwellers reside and travel. In 1999, Dr David Ander-son's laboratory at Wake Forest University began a study on Tern Island and the National Wildlife Refuge, now a part of the Papahanaumokuakea Marine Nation-al Monument, South Pacific. He was researching why globally albatross populations were crashing at 10 per cent, yearly. Using orbiting Argos Systems satellites and tiny radio transmitters taped between albatross wings, he and his team set forth to examine this catastrophe. Thousands of school children in Hawaii and around the world followed the birds with project email updates to 500 teachers in Australia, Canada, Estonia, Germany, Japan, South Africa and the US.

A Laysam albatross he tracked flew 39,980 kilometres (24,842 miles) across the North Pacific to find food for its chick in just 90 days. (She circled the globe once.) Flights across the North Pacific of other birds revealed that they made repeated trips from Tern Island and as far north as the Aleutian Islands. Another Blackfooted albatross made long repeated trips from Tern Island to San Francisco Bay and back. These observations eluci-dated how the availability of food affects these seabirds, how their reproduction rates and general population can be protected from tragic declines due to longline fishing fleets rapacious scouring of the Pacific Ocean for tuna and other fish quotas.

Albatross are monogamous, selecting a mate for life. The courtship can last longer than two years. The elaborate courtship dances are the most spellbinding and graceful that I've ever witnessed in three decades of observing nature. They include: beak-to-beak touching, repeated head shaking from "yes to yes" and "yes to no" gestures. They dance together increasing then decreasing tempos with widely exaggerated movements. It's indiscernible as to which partner leads. Bill clicking is common, interspersed with high-steps, followed by low steps with a lot of bill clacking in between. No two dances are ever the same. When the dance finishes, each partner bows, then the female walks away. They may sit quietly or dance with another bird, again. Albatross have the most intricate courtship of any non-human creature. Scientists believe the dance conveys important information such as stamina and strength, both exceptional indicators of health and vigour. When mating for life it's all about passing on "long-life" fitness genes of survival to future generations. Over a long lifespan, a prospecting female may spend up to one third of her time dancing onshore assessing males.

Royal and Wandering albatross begin breeding in their 14th year. The male will arrive at the breeding island first, about a week ahead of the female. When couples reconnect, they forgo the thrilling courting dance of the past, copulating within an hour of their reunion. They immediately take to the sea for a fortnight honeymoon enabling the female to gain additional nutrition to build her energy-rich egg. Do they stay together at sea? Feed one another? Scientists do not know. They arrive back to the breeding island within a couple hours of one another. A day later, the female lays one egg, weighing a half a kilogram (1.1 pounds). Then she leaves. It costs her plenty of nutrition, which she must immediately replenish. It turns out that males incubate the egg about one week longer than the female, building her body weight in order to feed the chick is of paramount importance for the dance of survival to succeed.

Parents take shifts on the nest. When the albatross first arrive on the island they are plump. The female looses about 12 per cent of her body weight from producing the egg, which she regains on her first foraging trip. A whopping 20 per cent of albatross body weight is lost during each incubation shift on land. At about 65 days the chick begins to break through the eggshell, sometimes it takes 24 hours or several days. Parents are purely bystanders they provide no physical help only (one assumes) moral support. Returning parents squirt a stream of gooey nutritious liquefied oil into the chick's throat. That stomach oil is powerful – calorically it is just slightly less than commercial grade diesel oil in its energy-punch. Each bird takes five of six parental shifts over the course of two months of feeding. By then the chick is an impressive ten-and-a-half kilograms (23 pounds).

Sixty-five per cent of eggs result in chicks ready to embark upon fledgling. About 10 per cent expire learning to fly on their first flight; Tiger sharks patrol offshore awaiting crash-landers. Those birds that make it past fledgling have a 93-98 per cent chance of reaching their 20th birthday. And many easily reach beyond 40 years as evidenced from leg bands and research dating back to the 1960s. During that time period from egg to fledgling, breeding pairs may only have spent ten days or less together. Many albatross breed only ever other year. Light-Mantled Sooty albatross raise one chick every four years, the lowest reproduction rate of any bird species.

The Hawaiian archipelago and its string of islands and atolls called Northwestern Hawaiian Islands, stretches for more than 1,600 kilometres (994 miles) from the bigger Hawaiian Islands. Ten islands ranging in size from Maro Reef, a single emergent rock, and Gardener Pinnacles of 0.02 kilometres^2 (0.008 miles^2), to Midway's Atoll of 6.2 kilometres^2 (2.4 miles^2), are essential habitat for six million breeding seabirds, 18 species, juveniles and non-breeders or approximately 14 million birds. Occupying 0.1 per cent of the Hawaiian land base area it's pivotal breeding grounds for 95 per cent of its seabirds including 500,000 pairs of Laysam and 50,000 pairs of Black-Footed albatross. There are 24 species of albatross with approximately 1.6 million breeding pairs. They only come ashore on 22 remote islands in the Southern Hemisphere and six island groups along the Hawaiian archipelago to breed. The seabirds of North-western Hawaiian Islands require an estimated 376 million kilograms (829 million pounds) annually of prey mostly fish crustaceans and squid from the surrounding ocean. The albatross alone consume 180 million kilograms (397 million pounds) of food.

Albatross are members of a large family called tube-nosed seabirds, which have hard tube-shaped nostrils on each side of the bill. An albatross bill has a sharp nail-like hook. Dense stiff feathers protect albatross from cold seas, gale force winds and blistering sun. They seek no shade during their entire lives, instead, they are exposed to the harshest extremes of heat, cold water and winds across the oceanic globe. These are some of the hardiest, thrifty critters on the planet. It's a good thing because they are globetrotters possessing Tour de France energy. They seldom fly more than 15 metres (49 feet) above the sea and they inhabit every open ocean except the Northern Atlantic. Albatross live in the windiest parts of the ocean between latitudes of 30° and 55°. Although Galapagos albatross breed near the equator foraging where the Humboldt Current upwells off Peru and Ecuador. Twenty of the 24 species of albatross live and breed in the Great Southern Ocean.

Albatross will dine on fish, fish eggs, crustaceans and jellyfish but predominantly they rely upon squid. There are 700 species of squid that use a form of locomotion similar to jet propulsion. These animals are dubbed by some of my colleagues as "honourary vertebrates" for their complex behaviour and exceptional eye sight. Their habitat ranges from sunlit reefs to deep, dark oceans, from finger nail-sized to the colossal squid, with the largest eyes in the entire Animal Kingdom, of the Antarctic Ocean.

About 27 species of squid provide albatross with their main food source. Squid die en masse after spawning, and about a day after perishing their bodies float to the surface. Squid livers release ammonia and they suddenly become buoyant. Disturbingly, humans now compete with albatross for their food, harvesting millions of tonnes of squid using night-lights to attract them. Astronauts have recorded a mass of lights from squid boats in the Southern Hemisphere rivaling those of west-coast South American cities.

They fly night and day at an average speed of 24 kilometres per hour (15 miles per hour). During the night, scientists conclude that albatross sleep by resting alternating halves of their brain. Most birds have a poor sense of smell but albatross have a potent olfactory system, in fact, it's one of the most sensitive to have ever evolved. These are the blood hounds of the sea. Albatross also look for diving flocks of terns and boobies signaling tuna. Tuna indicate larger fish, which also feed on squid. Albatross also look for flotsam, which is a rich source of flying fish eggs, loaded with protein. And they are always on the lookout for driftwood, now rare but they too are a veritable grocery stores stocked full of squid. The key - as in all life - for all species is patience, it begets more patience. Being in the right place at the right time pays off, big time, for albatross (as it does, by the way, for humans).

Albatross constantly search for the earthy fresh smell of phytoplankton, which feeds zooplankton providing food for smaller fish and those little fish feed on squid. Albatross rely upon smelling the food chain in order to survive. They can smell minute changes in water temperatures. Nutrients upwell when cold currents mix with warmer waters. Albatross also keep a sharp eye out for glowing lantern fish at night, as they too are indicators of squid, which feeds these bioluminescent beauties. When an albatross finds live squid, puffs of ink explode on the sea surface as ravenous birds nab their prey.

Since the 1800s humans have murdered millions of albatross, first it was the feather hunters who drove the Short-Tailed albatross to the brink of extinction, then military operations at Midway. Next were the driftnets

that decimated a quarter million, half were Sooty albatross. Now, in the North Pacific, the atrocious longlines
with hundreds of millions of hooks slaying tens of thousands of birds in just that sea each year. Distressingly,
if still alive and hauled into longline boats many albatross are savagely executed. "The fact is that the global
slaughter of marine wildlife is simply the largest massacre of wildlife on the planet," as Watson constantly
reminds me. This insane brutality and depraved worldwide slaughter disturbs me to my core. It's the equivalent of filling the Empire State Building 23 times, each
year, with nature's unrivaled maritime masterpieces,
demolished as bycatch and thrown disdainfully into the
sea!

The Great Southern Ocean and its Sub-Antarctic frontal
zone are fraught with gales and bone chilling, freezing
cold temperatures. How do albatross survive? Nobody
knows. But this much we can say: Where there's squid
there's albatross. The only reason why albatross must
fly so far is to find squid. There's simply no way to get
their chicks closer to that food source. So they breed
on isolated ancient islands safe from predators (except man). One Wandering albatross with chick in nest
logged a staggering single-round trip of 14,400 kilometres (8,948 miles) between feedings. And after breeding,
well, albatross do what they do best: Wander the seas. In
35 days, a Wandering albatross traveled 24,000 kilome-

tres (14,913 miles) from the Sub-Antarctic island South
Georgia to off-coast Argentina, then crossed the Atlantic to coastal South Africa and then proceeded onward
to Australia. Northern Royal, Chatham and Buller's albatrosses from New Zealand voyaged across the entire
Pacific Ocean in 10 days to forage along the Humboldt
Current off Chile and Peru. Other New Zealand birds including Northern Royal albatross forage over the Patagonia Shelf east of Argentina, continuing eastward onto
South Africa along a circumpolar route.

In the Great Southern Ocean on any given day there are
approximately 30 poacher boats, illegally harvesting
deepsea Patagonia and Antarctic Toothfish. These fish
species can live well beyond 50 years. The intolerable
result of these lethal longliners throughout the oceans:
17 of the 24 species of albatross are facing extinction.
When the Australian government delayed the legal
longlining season for a month, allowing the albatross to
feed their chicks first, they reduced death rates to near
zero. Kudos to Australian scientists and bureaucrats
who helped protect these splendid seabirds, obviating
grotesque deaths. As we will see in the following chapter albatross, like all other sea critters, are turning up
everywhere, bellies bulging with plastic.

Weather is one of albatrosses few natural killers. Adults
are able to cope with gales, but not nesting, fragile

chicks. Winds in excess of 40 to 70 knots blow eggs out of nests. Adults can also be buried by blowing sand, and drifting sand entombs chicks. Cold rains can chill chicks whose plumage is not yet waterproofed, killing them. Searing heat from El Ninos of the past decades has caused albatross to abandon nests in record numbers. Warmer ocean temperatures have caused more intense El Ninos. Rising sea levels from the occurrence of melting glaciers has been disastrous for albatrosses. According to Dr James Hansen, a distinguished climatologist, sea-level rise from melting glaciers during this century will range from 2,000 millimetres (79 inches) to a minimum of 500 millimetres (20 inches). All Hawaiian seabird colonies and nations of albatross will be displaced to sea. In the forthcoming years, normally windy places may experience less winds, and calmer regions are predicted to suffer more hurricanes. Changing winds will impair albatross's ability to forage the sea.

There are about 9 million albatross remaining on Earth. These most worthy sea aviators intrigue every child or student that I have ever encountered. Humans are exceptional problem solvers. Now is clearly the time for us to shine precluding the next chapter from being our "last" chapter.

The Great Oceanic Plastic Dump

The ocean surface covers in excess of 315 million kilo-
metres^2 (121.6 miles^2). Over the past half-century it has
become the largest, continuous, ever-growing garbage
dump in the history of Earth. It is so overwhelming and
incomprehensible that each day an additional 3.5 million pieces of plastic enter our oceans, or, according to
scientists from the University of California at Los Angeles, an estimated 18.1 million tonnes (20 million tons)
of plastic each year. Researchers from the University
of Western Australia recently reported that every square
kilometre of Australian surface seawater is contaminated with at least 4,000 tiny pieces of plastic. As rescuers
frantically searched for the disappeared Malaysian Air-
line Flight MH370 a couple thousand kilometres (1,243
miles) northwest of Perth one thing became very clear:
The Indian Ocean is full of millions of tonnes of plastic.
For those of us who work or sail on the seas they collectively have become a huge cauldron of pernicious plastic broken into "micro-plastics," or, diminutive pieces
resembling confetti weighing in excess of 700 million
tonnes (772 million tons). Their distribution is ubiqui-
tous, worldwide.

In 1997, Captain Charles Moore sailed from Hawaii to Los Angeles. He first reported the endless mass of plastic dubbing it "The Great Garbage Patch." It is now the equivalent size of continental Europe. Swirling in the North Pacific Gyre, its ocean currents and winds have essentially become a giant congested toilet bowl, regularly disgorging three metres (10 feet) of plastic onto Kamilo Beach on Hawaii's Big Island. The North Pacific Gyre is fueled by a sub-tropical high. It's one of five gigantic interconnected systems of oceanic currents. Incidentally, each of the other four gyres are stuffed full of micro-plastics, too. As we will see, micro-plastics are perfect sponges attracting poisons, ingested by all marine life and ultimately by humans. This is easily the most conspicuous global example of deleterious human behaviour requiring immediate international action!

In 1909, Leo Hendrik Bakeland created the first form of synthetic plastic, a phenol-formaldehyde compound he called Bakelite. Malleable when treated under pressure, rigid and insoluble when cooled, highly moldable, more durable than ceramics, lighter than metal, electrically non-conductive and heat resistant – no wonder it earned the moniker "material of a thousand uses." It wasn't until World War II that polyethylene (plastic bags, dispensable bottles), propylene (bottle caps, fishing gear) and polystyrene (take-away food containers) were invented, and, by the 1960s, being mass-produced. By 1979, the production of plastics in the US eclipsed that of steel. Today, globally we produce 280 million tonnes

(308.6 million tons) of plastic, annually.

Plastics are long chains of monomer hydrocarbon molecules. One of the principle ingredients of all plastics is crude oil. How much? Four per cent of the entire world supply or about 3.4 million barrels of oil, each day, are used to make them. In the US alone we throwaway two million plastic bottles every five seconds, 24/7. In addition, approximately 11 million kilograms (24.3 million pounds) of plastics go unaccounted for each year in America.

This much we know: 85 per cent of all plastics in the ocean are from land-based sources. There's at least six times more plastic than phytoplankton in all oceans, and according to the UN Environmental Programme a minimum of 46,000 floating pieces of plastic for every square kilometre of Earth's oceans in their entirety. In some oceans plastics exceed 30-metre (98-foot) depths. Plastics are sullying the remotest beaches and Watson told me: "My crew and I recently walked around a remote Tongan island. Not a soul living on it but we collected a great deal of plastic, bottles, fishing buoys, flip flops, lighters, toys, etc. There is simply no place to go where plastic does not befoul the beaches and the most destructive plastic is the nodules we can't see, because plastic does break down into tiny particles that look like plankton and this gets eaten by birds and fish and they die. Plastic shopping bags look like jellyfish under water and this kill turtles. It is a major problem and threat to our oceans."

When plastics enter the ocean, UV light breaks them down into micro-plastics. Those chunks of plastic about the size of a lentil have been chemically tested, worldwide. Each particle examined so far contained between one-thousands and in excess of a hundred-thousand times concentrations of the following poisons: methyl-mercury (neurotoxin), DDT (dichlorodiphenyltrichloroethane) (organochloride insecticide, carcinogenic), pyrethroid insecticides (toxic for dogs and humans), PCBs (polychlorinated biphenyl, known carcinogen), PBDE or Polybrominated diphenyl ethers, the backbone of flame retardants (carcinogenic), Biphenol-A (BPA) and phthalates (plastic softeners, endocrine disruptors called "gender benders" that induce both male and female sex organs on amphibians and fish) and TBT (tributyltin compounds – used as anti-fouling hull paint, highly toxic to all marine life, causes obesity in humans). In addition to the vigintillion pieces of micro-plastics polluting the oceans, there are quintillion small plastic pellets called nurdles, the feedstock of plastics, floating and absorbing toxicity throughout the oceans and eventually sinking to the seafloor. Scientists have recently found that lugworms on the seafloor have ingested micro-plastics, which were shown to transfer pollutants and additives to the worms, reducing health and biodiversity. Nurdles are shipped around the globe often spilled during transfer in and out of railway cars. Those spilled nurdles wind up in gutters and drains, eventually carried into the sea. In fact, some are even washing-up on the Antarctic shoreline. In just three days in 2006, 2.3 billion nurdles washed down the Los Angeles and San Gabriel River's emptying directly into the Pacific Ocean.

Unless we curtail our addiction to plastics, which per person in the US has dramatically increased from 103 kilograms (227 pounds) per person in 2001 to 148 kilograms (326 pounds) per person in 2012 (similarly for Australians), we too will choke on them. Scientists from the University of California predict that oceanic masses of plastics will increase to 32 billion tonnes (35.3 billion tons) a year, within three decades. And those toxic micro-plastics hang around for at least 400 years in the oceans.

In America only two per cent of the plastics are recycled (Australia recycles about four per cent), most plastics produced worldwide are earmarked for landfills. Already the US buries over 242 million tonnes (266.8 million tons) of trash annually or the equivalent of 6,750 Blue whales in volume, daily. There's no waste in nature, a flawless model to be emulated. My students and other students globally understand this concept. Students from

Yale University in 2012 reported discovering a fungus, *Pestalotiopsis microspora*, in the Amazon jungle that thrives in an oxygen-free environment and is able to feast upon polyurethane (rigid foam cushion).

It is time for humans to stop polluting the land and the sea. Earth's wild ecosystems are so worthy and in such dire need of protection. Watson carries it to an even higher level: "Defending ecosystems is more important than anything else. If the oceans die, we will all die. Therefore, saving fish, the seabirds and the plankton from plastic is more important than a cure for cancer. This type of position makes me politically incorrect, but that matters very little to me. I would prefer by far, to be ecologically correct."

The reality is that recycling plastics simply doesn't work, that's why so few of them in Australia, the US and elsewhere are recycled. Recycling weakens the plastic long chain molecules, compromising its structural integrity, completely. After one generation of recycling the plastic industry has inadvertently created a massive secondary market of exponential waste. Since the 1960s, Watson and the rest of us have seen it increase over 100 fold. Charles Moore will tell you: "No matter where you are, there's no getting over it, no getting away from it, it's a plastic ocean now, and we're putting everything in the ocean on a plastic diet."

I tell my students that whatever we do to the oceans we do to ourselves. The facts that the micro-plastics are sponges loaded with poisons are a clarion wake-up call for humans to reduce consumption and begin to reuse materials. Furthermore, burning coal to derive energy for our power plants in America, Australia, China and elsewhere is releasing upwards of 10 million tonnes (11 million tons) of mercury vapour into Earth's atmosphere, annually. When mercury vapour lands 18 months later it's winding up in the ocean. Bacteria transform the element into a toxic form that can be taken up by fish and other sea creatures known as methylmercury. Micro-plastics and nurdles are absorbing methylmercury, they resemble fish eggs consumed by sea life. Mercury is a powerful neurotoxin, and our oceans are overflowing with methylmercury. It's in seabirds at levels never witnessed before. On Australia's pristine Lord Howe Island, Flesh-footed Shearwater seabirds are turning up with bellies jam-packed full of hundreds of pieces of plastic, and blood laced with mercury at levels measuring 30,000 ppm. Some of those birds will die slower than 265 other marine species that suffocate hideously on plastics. Researchers from the Institute of Marine & Antarctic Studies in Hobart agree that the widespread toxic effects of ocean plastics on all sealife are far greater than previously thought.

The Great Pacific Garbage Patch is actually comprised

of two enormous masses of ever-growing plastics. The Eastern Garbage Patch churns between Hawaii and California. The Western Garbage Patch extends east of Japan into the western archipelago of the Hawaiian Islands. A narrow 10,000-kilometre (6,213-mile) long current called the Subtropical Convergence Zone connects the two patches. The humongous clockwise North Pacific Gyre is carrying plastics now over 70-years-old. A couple years ago, a colleague of mine found plastic in the stomach of a Laysam albatross off the US west-coast with a serial number, which traced a missing-in-action World War II seaplane shot down just south of Japan in 1944.

It's not just that 95 per cent of Lord Howe's Shearwaters now have bellies crammed with plastics that has caused the UN to issue a statement that, "marine plastics are a toxic time-bomb." As early as 1982, a Humpback whale beached itself along Cape Code, Massachusetts, entangled in 75 metres (246 feet) of a plastic monofilament fishing net, starving with its ribs visible – dying a couple hours later. In 2008, two Sperm whales were found stranded along California's mid-coast with stomachs distended. They had consumed over 150 kilograms (331 pounds) of monofilament fishing nets and plastics from computers, cellular phones, automobile bumpers, chairs and tables. Plastics are so rampant throughout our oceans that Laysam albatross return from foraging in the North Pacific and regurgitate plastic meals to their chicks. One chick had a stomach with contents of six disposable plastic lighters, a plastic comb, a plastic toothbrush, a complete syringe with a needle, small plastic flashlights and parts of plastic flip-flops in addition to plastic fishing tackle. On the other side of the world, along Britain's North Sea coastline a study on Fulmars found 95 per cent of these venerable seabirds had plastic in their stomachs with an average of 44 pieces per bird. A proportional amount in a human stomach would be the equivalent of two kilograms (4.4 pounds).

Each year over a half trillion single-use disposable plastic bags are manufactured globally and tens of millions of them are entering the oceans. My home state of California has banned all single-use disposable plastic bags effective 1 July 2015. By the way, in Australia, we use 6.9 billion single-use plastic bags that if tied end to end would encircle the equator 42.5 times, each year. Plastic bags, at first glance in the sea, appear like jellyfish. Tens of thousands of sea turtles are sucking plastic bags into their bodies and if they don't immediately choke they die a much slower and more agonizing death from the absorption of PCBs, methylmercury, BPAs, insecticides and flame retardants as they insidiously seep into their blood. In conjunction with an obstructed bowl, these animals die from septicaemia or blood poisoning. One study showed half the adult Leatherback turtles had plastic in their guts, while 70 per cent of Leatherbacks found dead along the Atlantic coast at Juno's Loggerhead Marinelife Center had blocked digestive systems from plastic bags and balloons, an excruciatingly painful death. Over 65 per cent of Florida's Loggerhead turtles examined had plastic in their esophagus and stomachs. Researchers from the University of Queensland found that the amount of plastic that Green turtles have ingested has nearly double over the past 25 years. From albatross to dolphins and from great whales to sharks, plastic bags are being mistaken for squid, a lethal mistake for all marine life. As a matter of fact, the UN Environmental Programme now estimates that plastic debris kills more than a hundred-thousand marine mammals, sea turtles, sharks and one-million seabirds, annually. The World Society for Protection of Animals reported that bigger pieces of plastic ensnare and entangle between 57,000 and 135,000 whales each year.

Plastics are turning up in every organism tested from lantern fish to jellyfish from mussels to clams and oysters. Recently, marine scientists with UKs National Oceanography Centre in South Hampton examined fish from the English Channel, 500 or so across 10 species including: Mackerel, Whiting, Poor Cod and Gurnard, they found plastics in the guts of all the species tested. According to researchers from the University of Western Australia, each year mega tonnes of micro-plastics are being consumed by fish worldwide and entering the ocean food web. Scientists from Sea Education Association, Woods Hole Oceanographic Institution, and the Marine Biological Laboratory have discovered a new ecological habitat of microbial communities invading micro-plastics dubbing it "plastisphere." They are watching it closely for movement of pathogens particularly the *Vibrio* bacteria – the genus that causes the pandemic cholera and other harmful algae species. In 2009, marine biologists from Scripps Oceanography Institute on their Scripps Environmental Accumulation of Plastic Expedition detected the first form of life benefitting from the profuse amount of accumulated plastics: Ocean striders. Remember these oceanic insects hitchhike around the globe on driftwood, but since there's so little driftwood floating in the Pacific, they have adapted to laying their eggs amongst the ever-growing noxious broth of plastic that humans have so obliviously created.

Scientists know that a small dose of poison bio-magnifies as it moves along the food chain toward the apex predators. So if Bluefin tuna, for example, are showing up with Japanese radioactive poisoning off the coast of California, as scientists have documented, and if humans consume them, it magnifies by up to 100,000 times. It would seem rather prudent to adopt Dr Victor Lindlahr's dictum: "You are what you eat" and reconsider eating fish and seafood for the foreseeable future. Before leaving plastics altogether consider the following: According to the Zurich Design Museum's exposition "Mermaid Tears" – fleece clothing leaves behind 1,900 micro-plastic fibres every time its washed, and that many cosmetic exfoliating creams or face scrubs and tooth pastes contain abrasive polyethylene and polypropylene balls of micro-plastics, which also wash down the drain and are accumulating in our rivers, lakes and oceans. Researchers from the University of New South Wales found micro-plastics in sediment samples from 27 different sites around Sydney Harbour. At one site, the concentration of micro-plastics was greater than that found outside a former plastics factory in Sweden. Procter & Gamble, Johnson & Johnson, Colgate, Unilever and L'Oreal are among the companies that are finally announcing plans to replace abrasive micro-plastics beads with biodegradable substances like ground-up stone-fruit pits, oatmeal and even sea salt.

So what can we do? According to Charles Moore, "All this bullshit about going out there and scooping this stuff up – you can't scoop this stuff up! No way in hell you're going to get that out of these – it's just not feasible." The famed-designer and billionaire James Dyson loves a challenge, so he's designed a giant vacuum-on-a-boat to suck plastic from the ocean. We will need thousands upon thousands of these barges converted for fierce open ocean conditions. But first things first, the only way to stop the further spread of plastics into the world's food chain is to reduce the amount of plastics we personally use, and support campaigns that demand companies take responsibilities for their products post consumer. Having witnessed first-hand the amassing of worldwide oceanic plastics over the past four decades Watson is cautiously optimistic "It is getting late. But perhaps there is still time to bring the oceans back to life because I am convinced that the impossible is possible. In 1962, the year he was sent to prison, the very idea that Nelson Mandela could one day become the President of South Africa was unthinkable and seemed thoroughly impossible. But it happened. The answers to our problems are out there. It's up to us to find them. In this struggle, there's no room for self-pity and we cannot afford the luxury of pessimism. Courageous, imaginative and passionate people can turn the impossible into the possible. Those people are you, me and anyone who has the desire to change things."

When I asked Watson, "What can be done about our suffocating oceans?" He told me that. "Creativity is the key to saving creation from our darker side and the key to a future of ecological harmony between humanity and the diversity of wondrous species we share this planet with." We both agreed that humans are smashing problem solvers and tremendous toolmakers. I was thrilled to hear that Sea Shepherd was involved in an exciting collaboration called The Vortex Project, which is removing ghost nets and tonnes of plastics from the oceans and beaches. Watson explained that, "The Vortex Project is a collaboration between eco-material innovator Bionic Yarn, Sea Shepherd Conservation Society and Parley -- for the Oceans. Using Bionic Yarn's unique fibres made from ocean plastic, denim brand G-Star is producing G-Star's "RAW for the Oceans," a line of denim with a purpose. Sea Shepherd is using scientific innovation and awareness-building to mobilise teams around the globe to help clean up oceans and beaches. Recycling, enhancing and reusing plastics for yarn and other elements in consumer products is smart and it is an excellent business model. There is no waste in nature. In order for 7.3 billion people to live on our planet we require a "closed loop" economy, whereby companies and consumers are rewarded for reducing waste and safeguarding our environment. The Vortex Project is all about harmonising the human economy with marine ecosystem health. Watson reminded that, "It is time humanity takes responsibility for our actions and cleans up the mess we've made. We hope this is the first of many meaningful collaborations to come."

On 18 October 2014, Sea Shepherd christened its latest research vessel in Marina Del Rey, California, naming it after award-winning actor and ocean activist Martin Sheen. Martin Sheen has campaigned for over two decades with Sea Shepherd and long-time friend Captain

Paul Watson. These two intrepid warriors have stood shoulder-to-shoulder opposing brutal bludgeoning of Harp seals along Canada's eastern seaboard.

Sheen told me that, "It's a huge honour and privilege to have a research ship named after me. The biggest risk and danger to the world today are plastics in our oceans. The *RV Martin Sheen* will conduct scientific research on ocean plastics to protect our oceans and all its sealife." The addition of the *RV Martin Sheen* to Sea Shepherd's fleet strengthens their research commitment and ability to protect the ailing oceans at a crucial time in the history of the human race.

A CSIRO study found that some of Australia's remote beaches were the most polluted. The study estimated more than 150 million pieces of rubbish littering Australia's sand and shores. More than three quarters of that rubbish was plastic. This has had a disastrous effect on over 600 marine species who then consume what researchers have termed "plastic food." Along Australia's shores scientists have found cigarette lighters, toothbrushes, pill bottles, and bottle caps in the stomach of birds. Sea turtles are also turning up with stomachs stuffed full of plastic. Shockingly, so far the record is 200 pieces of plastic found in a single bird.

The top items collected from the ocean's shoreline Ocean's Day (June 8, 2014) were: Cigarette butts, plastic bags, styrofoam food containers, plastic caps and lids, plastic bottles, paper-bags, plastic straws and stirrers, plastic cups, plastic plates and eating utensils, glass bottles and beverage cans. On Clean Up Australia Day 2014, thousands of Australians prevented millions of cigarette butts from entering the oceans. And for the first time those butts were separated into organic waste, which is ash, tobacco and the paper was composted in industrial composting. Is it possible to go one month without using single-use plastics when you shop? Earth Carers, New South Wales thinks so, and launched a successful online campaign called "Plastic Free July," their website is filled with terrific tips. In the meantime, if you are near a river, lake, sea or ocean, please lend a helping hand and prevent all discarded objects especially plastics from entering our waterways.

It is clearly incumbent upon every country on Earth to cut their land-based plastics off before they contaminate waterways, emptying into our ailing oceans that are dining on a petroleum-based curse whilst simultaneously suffocating. Let's us now turn 180° from this calamitous chapter and focus on nature's *magnum opus* of the sea: The whales.

Surreal Cetaceans

I guarantee you that spending time watching whales and dolphins in the wild will fill you with awe and tremendous joy. Today, marine science follows the paradigm of: "Do as little harm as possible in your studies of nature." Reverence for nature and in particular the sentient whales, have led to some outstanding discoveries. Interestingly, the 1986 message from Hollywood's blockbuster "Star Trek IV: The Voyage Home" – that in order to save Earth, whales must be protected – seems more valid today than ever before.

"Nature does not need us but rather we need nature," says Watson correctly. Consider what whales have recently shown us. Workers from the Zoological Society of London and Queen Mary University examined 156 Blue, Fin and Sperm whales swimming in the what Jacques Cousteau called "the world's aquarium," or, the UNESCO World Heritage Site, Sea of Cortez, due to its astonishing variety of life. The whales have shown scientists that the hole in the ozone layer is getting worse, allowing UV radiation to penetrate Earth's protective ozone shield, causing cancers and cataracts. From high-resolution photographs and studying whale skin samples, they concluded that whales are becoming sun burnt during time spent at the surface. It turns out that as temperatures on Earth continue to rise, unintended consequences of climate disruption are becoming more life threatening. Scientists from the Jet Propulsion Laboratory at California Institute of Technology showed one of the paradoxes of global warming, that is, as surface temperatures rise, upper stratosphere temperatures plummet, and lingering (banned in 1987) chlorofluorocarbons created a hole in 2011 greater than 1.8 million kilometres^2 (694,984 miles^2) in the ozone layer above the Arctic. A hole in the ozone layer above the Arctic has never been witnessed before. One thing is for certain: People spending more time outdoors are advised to wear sunscreen and protective eyewear.

Researchers from Harvard University and the University of Vermont have found that Humpback whales in the Gulf of Maine carry huge quantities of nitrogen and iron from the deep sea, where they feed, up to the surface and release it in flocculent fecal plumes. Essentially, Humpbacks function as "upward biological pumps." Humpback whales contribute more nitrogen to the Gulf of Maine than all the local rivers carrying nutrient-rich sediments combined, estimated at 24,000 tonnes (26,455 tons), annually. In turn, these nutrients, including iron, allow more phytoplankton to grow, which increases the food supply at the base of the marine food web, therefore promoting bigger fisheries and higher abundance where whales occur in greater densities. This irrefutably debunks the claim by Japan, Norway, Russia, Iceland, Denmark, South Korea and others that whales compete with their commercial fisheries. Instead, they enhance them.

There are between 1,100 and 1,600 Sperm whales living year-round in the Gulf of Mexico, mostly along the continental shelf feeding on squid, crabs, fish and sharks. In the spring of 2010, 794 million litres (209.8 million gallons) of oil with high concentrations of methane gushed into the Gulf from the BP Deepwater Horizon blowout. Researchers from Ocean Alliance and Sea Shepherd examined the Gulf ecosystem for residual toxicity, in particular within Sperm whales. Ocean Alliance has fortuitously been studying the Gulf Sperms since 2000, having established a benchmark to compare the health of these whales before and after the blowout from 2010 to 2013. Their results revealed disgracefully higher levels of heavy metals including: cadmium, aluminum, chromium, lead, silver, mercury and titanium within the Sperm whales. Furthermore, the Gulf Sperm whales are the most polluted to ever be recorded in any ocean. These whales are vividly showing scientists that the Gulf ecosystem has not recovered from the equivalent of 318 Olympic swimming pools filled with petro-leum plus an additional three Olympic swimming pools overflowing with Corexit oil dispersant. According to the eminent whale biologist Dr Roger Payne and lead member of the study, "The consequences are horrific for both whale and man. I don't see any future for whale species except extinction."

Scientists from the College of Atlantic in Maine brows-ing the photo-sharing site Flickr found identification markings on a Humpback fluke or tail taken by a Nor-wegian tourist whale watching at the breeding grounds near Île Sainte Marie off the east-coast of Madagascar, Indian Ocean in 2001. In 1999, that female was pictured in the breeding grounds off the Abrolhos Marine Na-tional Park, an archipelago of five islands with coral reefs off the southern coast of Bahia state, northeastern Brazil, Atlantic Ocean. The female Humpback swam at least 9,850 kilometres (6,121 miles), nearly a quarter of the globe. It was the longest documented movement of a mammalian ever recorded. Until then, Humpback mi-gration patterns were believed to be north/south rather than east/west. Was she responding to a distant com-plex song? Following prey? Exploring new breeding grounds? Or was she simply wandering as whales are so perfectly evolved for? We have a lot to learn from our cetacean friends!

Whales are maritime sentinels, revealing the health of the waters they swim through. Workers from Baylor University, Santa Barbara Museum of Natural History and the Smithsonian Institute have perfected a method of studying whale earwax, which similarly to tree rings shows a snapshot of the environment. In 2007, a 12-year-old Blue whale was struck and killed by a ship off Santa Barbara, California. The scientists extracted a 254-millimetre (10-inch) giant plug of earwax rich in lipids or specialised fats, laid down in 24 light and dark layers. The lighter colours were rich in lipids associated with abundant food whereas the darker bands connoted leaner times linked to fasting. The earwax showed a 400-fold surge in testosterone at the age of 10 when the male reached sexual maturity. And as he started to compete for a mate levels of the stress hormone cortisol spiked by 800-fold. Those layers of the earwax are analogous to its biography. Sadly, its earwax was loaded with 16 pollutants including: flame retardant, methylmercury, and several persistent organic pollutants particularly DDT – banned in the United States in 1972. This Blue whale was born in 1995, 23 years after the US ban. Ninety six per cent of the organic pollutants found in the earwax came from four phased-out pesticides and PCBs (used in coolants and insulating fluids). Levels of mercury soared twice within its lifetime: 2000 and again in 2005. Since the whale travelled back and forth along the California coastline, the researchers surmised that it swam through regions of highly toxic mercury poisoning. This Blue whale's biography is clearly telling scientists that the Pacific Ocean is rife with man-made toxicity.

Lastly, Narwhals, permanent residents of the Arctic, possess brains to body size just slightly smaller than humans. These extraordinary beauties of a beast dive greater than 1.5 kilometres (almost one mile) in pitch-dark, icy Arctic waters relying on sonar to hunt, only during the winter, Greenland Halibut. They spend up to three hours a day at least 800 metres (half a mile) from the surface, marvelously adapted to 80 atmospheres of pressure. Oceanographers from the University of Washington and Greenland Institute of Natural Resources tagged 14 adult Narwhals with sensors and determined that the temperatures of the Arctic Ocean was 1C (1.8F) warmer than previously recorded. The Arctic is warming at an unprecedented rate. In the 1980s the Arctic contained about 990,000 kilometres^2 (347,492 miles^2) of thick ice at least 5-years old. In September of 2012 only 57,000 kilometers^2 (22,007 miles^2) of such older, thicker ice remained. The Arctic has lost 97 per cent of its thicker year-round ice that existed just three decades ago.

Cetaceans are an anatomical classification of the whales based upon distinct eating capabilities. The great whales, or rorquals, as well as Right whales and others, are filter feeders consuming mega amounts of krill and small fish by using a baleen system or plates of spongy cartilage-like material hung from the upper jaw that beautifully sieves the water and collects the food. They are the largest whales in the seas. Toothed whales garb their prey with teeth and use suction of the mouth to pull them in. The largest toothed whales are Sperms. All 45 species of dolphins and their mistaken twins, the porpoises, are small-toothed whales. Orcas are the largest dolphin, with the second heaviest brains among marine mammals, after Sperm whales. There are 84 species of cetaceans represented by 14 families, all powered by strong horizontal tails.

Their earliest progenitors date back to the middle Eocene Epoch about 53 million years ago. Whales are seven-and-a-half times older than the earliest human ancestors. It wasn't until about 23 million years ago that whales split into two great groups: filter feeders (Mysticeti) and toothed creatures using sound to hunt and communicate (Odontoceti). Fossil skulls modified overtime to finely adjust to those behemoth Sperm whales. Nostrils, which first occurred on the top of the head, migrated to the rear forming the blowhole(s), a splendid adaptation to grab a fast breath on the move, a characteristic of the long distance travelers like Blues. In most mammals, including humans, the esophagus (throat) and trachea (wind pipe) are connected, which is why if you are not careful you can choke on food. In whales, the two pipes are separate. The esophagus leads from the mouth to the stomach. The trachea connects the blowhole to the lungs. Toothed whales have one blowhole, while baleen possess two. The tooth-substituted baleen system enabled these creatures to become immense as they consume prodigious quantities of mostly krill enmeshed in the plankton's web of life. For instance, a mature Blue whale consumes as much as 3.5 tonnes (3.9 tons) of krill each summertime day. Thick blubber offered tremendous insulation required for foraging in polar regions, this facilitated the growth of Earth's truest giants.

In the late Miocene era, or, more than five million years ago, gargantuan whales appeared and thrived until very recently. They dispelled the notion that gigantism is an indicator of extinction. Ice Age sea levels changed, yet even local food sources did not interrupt cetaceans' lives. Instead, they moved to more productive areas finding food despite an Earth enveloped within an icebox. Then, in the last Ice Age, The Pleistocene, it produced the newest and smallest member of the baleens, a "little" 13-tonne (14.3-ton) piked whale known as Minke. Whales have displayed extraordinary resilience to cataclysmic change until humans began mercilessly annihilating them.

Before we closely examine the New Zealand government's poignant 1982 declaration: "Like it or not, the whale is now a symbol of mankind's failure to manage the world's resources responsibly," let's get to know these surreal cetaceans.

Toothed whales hunt in some of the coldest, darkest waters in polar and abyssal oceans. For baleen whales (except subtropical Bryde's), summer in the polar seas is feeding time because the remainder of the year is spent swimming a quarter the way around the Earth where they mate and sustain their young. During the first three weeks of a Blue's life it adds over 115 kilograms (254 pounds) a day, the fastest growth spurt of its life. Every summer, the toothed Belugas congregate by the thousands in the warmer, shallow estuaries of Canada's Churchill and Mackenzie Rivers. The warmth triggers pituitary hormones. These gorgeous near-white Leviathans rub against round cobbled riverbeds, shedding their old, yellowish winter skin. Belugas are the only cetaceans capable of facial expression. Their lips and the melon of fat that forms the forehead are highly mobile. At times they appear to smile or even frown. Arctic Narwhals travel and forage in groups of a couple dozen and occasionally amass by the thousands. They have a peculiar habit of drifting, lazily in a variety of positions including on their sides, belly and even head down.

Humpbacks belong to the regal rorquals all endowed with huge expandable throat plates for filter feeding. Rorquals are known to live for a long time e.g. Fins can live for at least 140 years. Blue, Minke, Sei, Bryde and Fin share the same sleek tapering lines that jet fuselages mimic. Humpbacks, on the other hand, defied the trend displaying a stockier body with a knobby head, and the longest flippers of any cetacean. Humpbacks are the slowest of the rorqauls with a top speed of about 15 knots – whalers decimated these colossal creatures.

Have you ever witnessed a breathtaking breach? It's a way that a whale demonstrates its strength and stamina to prospective mates as judged by the energy of the breach and the sound and frequency of the splash. Humpbacks breach more frequently than almost any other whale, often leaving the water completely, an awesome feat considering they're in excess of 36 tonnes (40 tons). As they breach the rostrum or snout is tilted horizontal toward their tail so they fall either on their backs or sides. Only one in five breaches turns into a belly flop.

All toothed whales navigate the seas with the most sophisticated high-frequency sonar system unrivalled by anything on the planet, man-made or otherwise. They send out noises called "click trains," which sound like old creaky doors. As these complex sounds called echolocation move through the water they encounter objects, bouncing back shapes and contents to be deciphered by very large brains.

Sperm whales are extraordinary deep divers. At over twenty metres (66 feet) long and 55 tonnes (60.6 tons) males are twice the size of females, spending the first quarter century getting large by eating daily 1,000 kilograms (2,205 pounds) of crabs, tuna, Antarctic Toothfish, squid, Cuttle fish, and their preferred prey colossal squid. These sharp-beaked, 25-metre (82-feet) long, 600 kilograms (1,541 pounds) of a meal, with dozens of tentacles outfitted with retractable razor-sharp claws and fearsome toothed rings the size of small dinner plates, line-up in the battle of Earth's truest titans. It's a raging free-for-all-fight; judged by the ringed-scars on Sperm whale heads' these fierce beasts certainly don't go quietly. It's why Sperm whales evolved the thickest skin of 350 millimetres (13.8 inches) in the entire Animal Kingdom: Protection from piercing tentacles.

In order to chase giant squid to the end of the ocean, Sperm whales excel at deep-sea diving. Massive rectangular heads evolved to hold 1,900 litres (502 gallons) of spermaceti oil-filled capsules, believed by some to focus sonar clicks, assist in buoyancy and promote deep-sea dives. As Sperm whales dive, lungs collapse, water temperature drops, cooling the spermaceti to its freezing point a couple degrees below the whale's core temperature, where it turns into a waxy solid, slightly shrinks yet increasing its over all density enabling them to reach a mind-boggling 3.19 kilometres (1.98 miles) beneath the sea surface. Males can dive for longer than 45 minutes. As they ascend from the deep, blood vessels carrying the whale's core temperature melt the spermaceti wax, adjusting buoyancy while surfacing.

Females live in warmer waters in groups of dozens, close relatives including aunts, sisters, daughters and mothers. Extended families protect calves from Orcas or Great White sharks, placing them in a tight circle guarded by the snouts of adults like spokes on a wheel, defending them with large extremely powerful tails. Solitary males migrate from polar seas to roam amongst female aggregates to breach, mate and dance. Mothers teach calves how to communicate in codas, keeping social group together. It's wonderful to watch pods of Sperm whales sleeping vertically, head down or to see such a large gathering in a tight school at the surface after morning forage, caressing one other with their mighty lower-toothed jaws and flippers.

The small-toothed whales are equally intriguing. Once upon a time, tens of millions of dolphins roamed the oceans in freedom. Superpods in excess of 100,000 Bottlenose dolphins were common, unlike today. Just like humans, dolphins sleep as much as a third of each day by bunching tightly together, as one lazy eye per dolphin remains open and although asleep, their slow methodical echolocatory clicks scan their environment for sharks and other predators. Moreover, dolphins are innovative when faced with a new scenario or situation. This goes way beyond genetic programming or behaviour. Innovation allows rapid assessment of a new situation and reaction to it. Dolphins easily understand gestures, similar to sign language that chimpanzees are also able to learn. Humans and Bottlenose dolphins appear to be the only known animals to spontaneously interpret images on a screen without prior teaching. Dolphins are capable of highly flexible behaviour, and therefore are considered intelligent. Furthermore, Bottlenose dolphins remember the signature whistle of each individual pod member even when separated for more than two decades, making them champions for the longest memory among non-human species according to scientists at the University of Chicago. Interestingly, adult dolphins discipline their misbehaved juveniles by driving them to the seabed and momentarily holding them there. Dolphins, like ravens, crows, ants, crocodiles, gorillas and chimpanzees, use tools to assist when foraging. For example, along the Great Barrier Reef, I've seen Bottlenose dolphins fossicking the seabed using echolocation, probing their rostrum (or nose) up to

750 millimetres (29.5 inches) into the floor. In order to protect their nose and face from spines and stingers they use a sponge whilst hunting for buried bottom-dwelling fish. Juvenile Bottlenose learn this behaviour from their mothers. Interestingly, just like human teenagers experiment with hallucinogenic drugs so too do juvenile Bottlenose. They carefully manipulate pufferfish (rather aptly-named) to release its toxins, pass it amongst one another like a joint of marijuana and then drop into a trance. This deliberate behaviour appears to carry some of the hallmarks of human drug use. The largest of this clever clan of dolphins is the counter-shaded black and white Orcas with stable social units comprised of closely related males and females including brothers, sisters, fathers and mothers. They remain together for the duration of their lives of over 65 years, mating when two or more pods come together to socialise. Lastly, "It is interesting to note that while some dolphins are reported to have learned English – up to 50 words used in correct context – no human being has been reported to have learned Dolphinese," remarked the late famed astrophysicist Dr Carl Sagan.

In early spring of 2012 off-coast of Malibu, California my Chesapeake Bay retriever, Naio, and I had the rare privilege of getting extremely close to the largest animal on Earth – an exalted Blue. For over a-half-an-hour this beauty, equivalent in size to 59 African elephants, remained within metres of our dingy - we were awed - soaked from the spray of its one-and-a-half-metre (5-foot) wide blowholes shooting water resembling sheaves of wheat 8 metres (26 feet) into the air. It totally thrilled us. It's dark eyes, sea scent, unearthly groans and complex, contralto voice was truly mesmerising and life altering. Blue whales are the monarch of the seas: Invincible yet gentle. With a heart weighing 450 kilograms (992 pounds) or the size of a Volkswagen Beetle they pump 6,400 kilograms (14,110 pounds) of blood, providing strength to enormous tails rivaling 500 horsepower outboard motors, these 190-tonne (209-ton) giants (twice as heavy as the largest known dinosaur) cruise at 26 knots for two hours and race at 37 knots for ten minute intervals. That morning with the Blue was the most humbling experience of my life. It conveyed a message to me for our species: A message of respect for one another: Respect for every strand within nature's magnificent interdependent web of life.

The cornucopias of small organisms like worms, tunicates, amphipods and coruscations along the muddy, sediment-rich seafloor fed by driftwood are a mouthwatering buffet, frequented by two other filter feeders: Gray's and Bowhead's. Gray's dive at 45° angles, rolling so that one side of their mouth drive into the sediment as they suck the silt and water into their mouths. As they surface plumes of silt are expelled before they harvest their delicious smorgasbord. Evidence of prior trips to their bountiful buffet is clearly visible along the pockmarked seafloor. Both Grays and Humpbacks are adaptable feeders visiting kelp forests where Herring lay millions of eggs onto frowns during mass spawning. I've marveled in southern Californian under-water when these wondrous whales harvest the protein-loaded eggs by gingerly clamping their massive maws onto the kelp fronds, combing them through their baleen where hundreds of thousands of eggs are captured, especially careful not to damage or uproot the kelp. Humpbacks also employ clouds of bubbles to corral fish and krill, individually or in cooperatives rounding up the prey with helical patterns of bubbles, hypnotically drawing the fish or krill into the centre of the spirals where the whale(s) swim from beneath - feasting upon their scrumptious seafood banquet.

Bowheads are very mysterious creatures they live in the Beaufort and Bering seas between Russia and Alaska and Fram Strait off Greenland. Recently, scientists discerned the whales' ages by studying changes in amino acids in the lenses of their eyes. Astoundingly, they discovered Bowheads live for at least 211 years – the longest of any whale species and very likely the longest living of all 5,416 known species of mammals. Four centuries of commercial whaling decimated Bowhead populations. Researchers from the University of

Washington's Applied Physics Laboratory and NOAA are researching the sounds of the critically endangered Bowhead whales in Fram Strait off Greenland's coast. They found that the Bowhead's (believed to be males) sing 60 unique songs within one year. The following year they have a new repertoire of completely different songs, which is unprecedented in other whale species. These socially complex creatures produce a beautiful underwater chorus more reminiscent of songbirds rather than any other kind of whales. The song diversity, loudness and duration infer that western Fram Strait is an important wintering ground as well as a mating area. During the winter they swim in 24-hour darkness with over 95 per cent ice cover. Can one individual remember 60 songs? Or rather do individuals within the group share those 60 songs? The answers are unknown. Bowheads are truly charismatic, intelligent animals.

Cetaceans, just like people, simply enjoy having fun. Southern Right whales raise their flukes above the water at a right angle to the wind and use them as sails – allowing them to be blown along by the wind, often swimming back to the starting point and doing it, again. Dusky dolphins sometimes after a big Anchovy meal will locate an unlucky gull sitting on the ocean surface, digesting or preening, they sneak-up underneath, grab the birds leg and pull them a metre (3.3 feet) under water, opening their jaw and letting them go, the distraught bird floats to the surface like a bobbing cork, agitated it quickly takes to the air, while the devious Dusky leisurely swims away.

Whales are enchanting just ask any child. Why are they still being persecuted, despite an international moratorium in 1986? It is infuriating that since 1986 Japan, Norway, Russia, Iceland, USA, South Korea and Danish Faroe Islanders have barbarically slaughtered in excess of 48,000 whales. And worse, London-based Environmental Investigation Agency claims more than one million small-toothed whales, including dolphins and porpoises have been slaughtered off Japan in the past 70 years. Indeed some humans intend to continue the "War Against Nature" until there are no more whales or dolphins.

Well, with Watson and his fearless crew who are more than willing to lay down their lives for the whales, this War rages on. So far, Sea Shepherd has saved more than 7,500 whales in the Antarctic from Japanese grenade-tipped harpoons. And by the way, since Japan sells each whale for $250,000, Sea Shepherd has prevented the Japanese government from making $1,878,250,000! For the Japanese, Norwegian, Russian, Icelandic, South Korean and Danish whale poachers, I quote former leader of the Greens, Senator, and former Chairman of Sea Shepherd Australia, Dr Bob Brown, "Stoking your boilers is the perverse idea, which some people never grow out of, that you are closer to supremacy over nature if you kill other creatures bigger, faster or more mysterious than yourselves, no matter how un-threatening, amiable or technologically innocent those creatures may be." The year 2013-14 marked Sea Shepherd's 10th campaign "Operation Relentless" to protect the threatened and endangered whales of the Southern Ocean Whale Sanctuary. Watson audaciously responds to Japan and all other nations that still slaughter whales: "We protect the interest of our clients. Our clients are not people; they are whales and other marine species that are exploited and exterminated to serve the cultural or economic interests of humans." Moreover, Watson is convinced that, "Sea Shepherd Australia needs another ship, a ship that is long range and can exceed 25 knots. If such a ship can be secured and returns to the Southern Whale Sanctuary when the Japanese commence whal-ing in December of 2015, along with SSS Steve Irwin, SSS Bob Barker and SSS Sam Simon, I think the Japa-nese whaling fleet can be shut down 100 per cent."

It's incongruous that Japan still hunts whales when only one per cent of the Japanese population eats whale meat with over 6,000 tonnes (6,614 tons) of it currently being cryoprotected in deep-freezers. The Japanese whaling industry is an archaic, subsidised blood lust, driven by a political sense of entitlement. The fact is the oceans belong to the commons meaning that beyond the 322-kilometre (200-mile) territorial limit (UN Convention of the Law of the Sea) every denizen on Earth is a rightful stakeholder. Since 1986 Japan has hunted endangered whales (Fins and Humpbacks) under an IWC loophole of "scientific research," when the entire scientific community does not condone lethal research – something that was frowned upon almost a half century ago. "Japan targets endangered whale species in an established whale sanctuary in violation of the international moratorium on whale hunting, in opposition to the Australian federal court (ruling whaling in the Southern Ocean is illegal), in violation of the Convention of International Trade in Endangered Species of Wild Fauna and Flora and the Antarctic Treaty," says an indignant Watson who was vindicated as of 31 March 2014 with the final ruling by the International Court of Justice (ICJ). Incidentally, Japan has been buying votes at the IWC for decades including paying poorer countries like landlocked Laos, Africa, Solomon Islands in the South Pacific and Nevis and St Kitts in the Caribbean.

Japan's "scientific whale research" is overtly flawed. If, in fact, they were testing a hypothesis then their factory boat the *Nisshin Maru's* reaction to harassment by the Sea Shepherd ships during the 2012-13 whaling season would have ended the research sampling for that season. Instead, the *Nisshin Maru* fled, followed by one of its catcher boats, to the other side of the Antarctic continent, thousands of kilometres from its designated research area where it resumed harvesting piked whales. A true research programme is based upon systematic, pre-planned sampling in a designated area within a designated time frame. Japan's "lethal research" of rorqual and piked whales in the Antarctic has nothing to do with "scientific research."

In the meantime, US President Barack Obama has instructed officials to continue applying pressure on Iceland to comply with the whaling moratorium introduced by IWC in 1986. Obama, in a note to his cabinet officers, said senior delegations and officials meeting with the Icelandic government's representatives should remind them that if the North Atlantic nation wants to cooperate with the US then it must change its policy on whaling. Recently, the Icelandic government quietly increased their quota by authorizing the death warrants of 770 endangered Fin in addition to 1,145 threatened Minke whales over the next five years. This is incongruous since only 3 per cent of Icelanders even eat whale meat. So Iceland's only whaling company is now left murdering more sentient endangered whales to feed a burgeoning dog food market in Japan. The Director of Sea Shepherd Australia, Jeff Hansen summed up the prolonged global looting spree of our oceans this way: "These whale poachers have no respect for the global moratorium and the wishes of the majority of people on this planet that want to see an end to whaling. Whales are worth far more to us alive than they ever did from whaling, especially now with the explosion of the global whale watching industry and the sheer importance whales play in the health of our oceans. Iceland increasing their murdering quota of endangered Fin whales to be sold to Japan, where much of the whale meat will end up as dog food, is a complete lack of respect for these beautiful, intelligent and socially complex mammals, a complete lack of respect for the International Union for the Conservation of Nature and a complete lack of respect for our children that want to grow up in world with the great whales." Iceland exported whale meat worth $11M to Japan in 2011.

Japan is claiming that Watson has violated laws and treaties by engaging in piracy against their whale-killers. In February 2013, Judge Alex Kozinski of the Ninth US Court of Appeals in San Francisco likened Watson's actions in the Southern Ocean Whale Sanctuary to those of a pirate. "We are compassionate pirates, we go after the pirates who are motivated by greed and profit. The Sea Shepherd code of honour prohibits injuring or killing our enemies and dictates that we act within the framework of the international conservation laws, while at sea we oppose only illegal exploitation of maritime life," says Watson in response. And after 37 years, Sea

Shepherd Conservation Society is proud of their unblemished record.

The new moon of 31 March 2014 ushered in a long overdue win for the whales of the Great Southern Ocean and Sea Shepherd Conservation Society. The ICJ upheld Australia's bid to ban Japanese whaling in the Antarctic Ocean. The court found, 12 votes to 4, that Japan's whaling programme was not scientific research as defined under IWC rules. "As a state that respects the rule of law... and as a responsible global community, Japan will abide by the decision of the court," Japan's Chief Negotiator Koji Tsuroka said outside the UN's top court in The Hague. One immediate outcome from this ruling was Rakuten, Japan's biggest online retailer, announced that it would no longer sell whale and dolphin meat. All citizens hope that Japan will abide by the ruling and leave the whales to migrate through their icy sanctuary in peace. If, on the other hand, Japan returns to illegally poach threatened and endangered whales, Watson told me, "Sea Shepherd Global will intercept them, uphold international law and protect the whales."

On 11 April 2014 in a blatant show of defiance of the recent landmark ruling in The Hague by the ICJ, Japan's Institute of Cetacean Research (ICR) filed court briefs stating they intend to return to hunt whales in the Southern Ocean Whale Sanctuary for the 2015-

2016 season with a newly designed "research" programme and will seek a permanent injunction against
Sea Shepherd USA, despite the fact the USA en-
tity is no longer operating in the Southern Ocean,
and will also seek to enjoin other Sea Shepherd
entities. When I asked Watson about this he said, "When
the ICJ verdict was issued, I knew that although it was
a great victory that vindicated our opposition to illegal
whaling in the Southern Ocean, I could see the potential
for the ICR to re-write their programme and to return.
My prediction was they would return for the 2015-2016
season. It seems that this is exactly what they intend to
do. The statement Japan issued that they would comply with the ICJ ruling was I believe insincere. Japan
has a history of duplicity with regard to whaling. I fully
expect that Sea Shepherd Global will be prepared to return to the Southern Ocean in December 2015 to once
again defend the integrity of the Southern Ocean Whale
Sanctuary."

Clearly, the ICR is unsettled not only by the favour-
able ICJ ruling but also by Commissioner Peter Shaw's
recent recommendation to the Ninth Circuit Court
that Sea Shepherd USA not be held in contempt. In
their court brief, the ICR threatened: "If the Ninth
Circuit finds it was not Defendants who committed
contempt, then Plaintiffs may need to add to this action the parties who did commit the contempt." They

also noted: "Plaintiffs expect additional parties they may seek to add to this action would include foreign parties." However, how they intend to bring foreign entities before a US court has yet to be seen. Furthermore, Tasmanian Greens Senator Peter Whish-Wilson said Prime Minister Tony Abbott left Japan, which he visited on an April 2014 trade mission, without raising the whaling decision. "We warned the Abbott Government before and after the ICJ decision that Australia would need a strong diplomatic response to cement the result. All Australians will be devastated to hear that the whalers are planning to return. The Government said that they would put trade ahead of whales, and it is clear that this is what has occurred," remarked an angry Whish-Wilson.

On 9 June 2014, Japan's Prime Minister Shinzo Abe told the parliament that he would boost his efforts to recommence commercial whaling in the Southern Ocean Whale Sanctuary despite the ruling on 31 March by the ICJ, upholding Australia's bid to ban whaling in the sanctuary. Japan's state-owned lethal whaling institute ICR intends to use three months of surveying from the Southern Ocean Whale Sanctuary beginning in December 2014 to collect non-lethal sight surveys, distant angle estimation experiments, photo identifications and biopsy skin samples to justify poaching protected Southern Hemisphere whales. The brazen gall and effrontery of these loathsome ocean-killers hath no bounds. The fact that they are attempting to feign science to collect population density numbers for their intended December 2015 bloodbath has fooled no one except some of the bureaucrats at the IWC. It takes years of meticulous, reproducible sampling to amass an accurate estimate of population health and dynamics. Sadly, this masquerade smudges the rigours of science and the oath my colleagues take to perform excellence for the betterment of humanity.

On 16 September, Japan declared war against the whales within the international Southern Ocean Whale Sanctuary. Japan decided to ignore the majority ruling of the IWC that has specifically condemned their continued invasion into the sanctuary. New Zealand has put forward a resolution to preclude Japan from killing any more whales within the sanctuary and Australia's Environment Minister Greg Hunt supports it. "Our hope and our belief is this is the moment when the world can respectfully work to end the practice of commercial whaling or scientific whaling which has been justified where as in reality it's simply commercial whaling by another name," says Hunt.

Since the 1986 world moratorium on whaling, Japan has massacred over 15,000 whales. This we know with certainty, as Captain Siddharth Chakravarty of SSS Steve

Irwin clearly puts it: "The Japanese whaling industry has once again shown that they have no regard for international law. The poachers have already announced that they will be returning to the Southern Ocean Whale Sanctuary to continue with their illegal lethal research programme. The ICJ ruled as recently as the 31st of March that it found no merit in Japan's bloody science. And yet, in the face of international opposition, the Japanese whalers intend to bring bloodshed through the gates of the whale sanctuary."

The oceans are dying quickly. Its time the world's leaders band together to protect our priceless life-support system instead of turning a blind eye and hastening its demise. Sea Shepherd will monitor Japan's so called non-lethal sampling this forthcoming 2014 austral summer. Jeff Hansen, the Managing Director of Sea Shepherd Australia told me, "Japan wants to ignore the Federal Court of Australia and the International Court of Justice and the IWC to brutally slaughter highly intelligent and social complex beings in an established whale sanctuary. If the governments of the world still refuse to challenge Japanese whale poachers on the high seas, then Sea Shepherd will meet them head on in defense of the whales."

In 2013, when a US court ruling forced Watson to step down as Antarctica's campaign leader of "Operation

Zero Tolerance," legendary conservationist, Dr Bob Brown, took over "Operation Zero Tolerance," leading the most successful ever direct-action campaign to protect the great whales against the Japanese ocean-killers. Both of these remarkable men possess a unique trait of grit; the quality of being able to sustain their passion to protect our oceans and forests; and work incredibly hard, over really disappointing long periods of time. They are global heroes because they pursued protecting our planet against all odds.

The Japanese government has kept its people disinformed with pro-whaling campaigns, and the Japanese media (for the most part) are pro-whaling likening the anti-whalers to terrorists. It's wrong that Japan siphoned $30 million from the tsunami 2011 Earth Quake Recovery Fund to subsidise its imprudent whaling programme. The Taiji dolphin massacre is vile and along with the Danish Faroe Islands long-finned Pilot whale massacre they are two infamous and appalling spectacles of the bloodthirsty "War Against Nature." In addition, some juveniles are taken away for sale to dolphinariums, "The idea that dolphinariums are an educational tool is a heresy. A dolphinarium is a circus where the animals are condemned to die after living out their bleak existence. The time I spent in prison taught me that incarceration is a form of torture. It gave me a sense of how much animals must suffer when they are in captivity. In my opinion they are better off dead. What's more, the emergence of aquariums and dolphinariums in Africa, Asia, South America and Eastern Europe is resulting in increased rates of capture from natural environments," says an empathetic Watson.

Distressingly, dolphins are turning up in Japan with PCBs levels of 140 times above the "safe" limit and methylmercury poisoning over 85 times past the "safe" level, and instead of tracing that poison, Japan allows its citizens to consume it. This is particularly shocking in light of the recent signing of the Minamata Convention on Mercury in Japan. Mercury permanently damages the central nervous system; no animal should ever swallow mercury because it's a hideous poison. As early as the year 2000, whale meat contaminated form PCB's, mercury, dioxins and other heavy metals were identified in the Japanese School Lunch Programme. It was removed but Japan still sells toxic dolphin meat throughout its nation. One 70-year-old man tested had mercury poisoning from eating contaminated dolphins, his blood was 80 times beyond "safe" mercury levels. According to Elsa Nature Conservancy, Japan "The Government of Japan's stubborn reluctance to relinquish this archaic industry is not only driving threatened marine species towards extinction, but is endangering the health of its people."

Equally disturbing is the annual Faroe Islands Grindadrap (translation "whale murders"). It is truly the most repugnant, deranged and evil ecocide touted as a ritual that I am aware of. Not only is it psychopathic behaviour, but also deleterious to the entire population of Faroese. In 2008, The Faroe Island's Chief Medical Officer announced that the long-finned Pilots that were brutally corralled, then mutilated off the shoreline, were laced with toxic levels of methylmercury, PCBs and DDT. The Chief Medical Officer deemed all long-finned Pilots unsafe for human consumption. He noted that ingesting long-finned Pilots blubber or meat would result in: fetal neural damage, high blood pressure, impaired immunity in children, increased rates of Parkinson's disease and circulatory complications in both children and adults. The fact that Denmark's Navy and Police condone the shocking annihilation of these remarkable mammals when the European Union, (of which they are a member) strictly forbids hunting cetaceans is rank hypocrisy, especially since these long-finned Pilots are toxic and unfit for human consumption. In 2013, bloodthirsty Faroe Islander's brutally slashed and slowly killed 1,104 long-finned Pilots. In July of 2014, Sea Shepherd mounted "Operation GrindStop" lead by two intrepid women: Lamya Essemali of France, and Rosie Kunneke of South Africa, spearheading a small group of unarmed, non-violent compassionate volunteers to protect the intelligent, socially complex, sentient long-finned Pilots.

Watson tells people in his Ted Talk: "The method used to kill whales would never be tolerated in an abattoir. It takes anywhere from 10 to 45 minutes for the whale to die after being hit by an explosive-tipped harpoon," The bloody and senseless right of entitlement by the Japanese fisheries must end. Dolphins and whales play a crucial ecological role in the health and wellbeing of our oceans. They are the mammalian "Doctors of the Sea" essential for sealife as we know it. Baleen whales act as upward biological pumps promoting phytoplankton, which stimulates fisheries. Toothed whales cull the old and weak ensuring high levels of fitness amongst their prey; preventing diseases from becoming epidemics throughout the oceans.

Do the Japanese have it within them to stop persecuting the whales and dolphins? It's a question that I posed to Watson, "I hope so. In 1977 we opposed the whalers in Australia and they stopped whaling in 1978. This whaling nation has become the strongest voice for whales of all nations. Japan can also change from a whale-killing nation to a whale respecting nation. The problem with Japan is the same as Spain. Both nations incorporate seafood as a major part of there so called "food culture." If they carry on they won't have their food culture and we won't have whales, dolphins, sharks and fish."

After more than four decades you can't help but admire Watson's courage of conviction, "I know whaling is wrong. I know killing everything in the crippled, gasping oceans is wrong. I don't give a damn about any bogus science and all the legal considerations of chicken shit bureaucracies. I know stopping killing is the right thing to do and I'm going to stop it devil take the consequences." Humans have remorselessly slaughtered whales; populations have not rebounded after 200 years of continuously flailing them. Furthermore, we capture and sentence them to torturous, drugged existences within dolphinariums; man-made poisons are rife throughout all their oceans; 21 million kilometres (13 million miles) of hooked fishing-gear and monofilament lines constantly entangle and drown them; plastics suffocate them; ships repeatedly strike them; naval-sonar as well as oil and gas exploration-sonar relentlessly blasts them and shatters their ear-drums causing mass strandings; human-induced climate disruption has prevented nutrients from upwelling and growing phytoplankton thereby impinging upon their life support system which provides them with food; we mine the plankton for its krill thus denying them their food; we incessantly burn fossil fuels forcing acidification of the oceans that destroys their habitat; and we continue to rapaciously hunt them into extinction as Japan, Norway, Russia, Iceland, Denmark and others display an abominable sense of entitlement and egregious disrespect for the pinnacle of marine mammal evolution that miraculously has stood the test of 53 million rigorous years of evolution: It is one of the darkest and most contemptible moments in the fleeting history of the human race.

On 17 May 2013, India's Ministry of Environment and Forests banned the use of dolphins, porpoises and all other whales for public entertainment and forbid them from being held captive anywhere in India. They declared cetaceans as "Non-Human Persons" and protected them because they are extremely intelligent creatures. On 24 February 2014 the Malibu City Council, California proclaimed that all dolphins, porpoises and whales that pass its Pacific shoreline have the right to life. Malibu is the first American city to protect cetaceans. It is indeed time for a worldwide amnesty for all cetaceans.

There are two final things I'd like to leave you with before outlining my short plan on healing the seas and ultimately the human race. First, consider that Taiwanese, Korean and Chinese tourists are flocking to Japan. The seas surrounding the Japanese archipelago are gorgeous and the potential for eco-tourism from visiting the wild Snow monkeys and hot springs of Hokkaido's mountains to whale watching including Muroran in Hokkaido, Kochi Prefecture on Shikoku, Ogasawara Island and Okinawa is an opportunity whose time has come. In 2008, 13 million people from 119 countries paid $2.1 billion to see the whales in the wild. Worldwide, whale watching tourism is growing at 10 per cent per annum. Don't you think after getting to know the cetaceans that it's time to end the "War Against Nature" in particular against whales and dolphins, and grant amnesty to glorious creatures that are helping us to survive on our blue planet?

After the ancestors of the whales returned to the sea their hind limbs shrank to a few tiny bones floating within their tail muscles. Their forelimbs developed into pectoral fins used so effectively to steer themselves through the water. Within the cetacean's pectoral fins are a set of bones resembling a human hand – a wrist and four or five splayed fingers. Are these the creatures that humans would have been had we remained in the water?

The last words belong to Captain Watson who's spent a lifetime at sea with these sublime, supreme giants and one in particular that spared his life enabling him to fulfill his mission over the past four decades.

The Whale

By Captain Paul F. Watson

Upon the billowing shroud of the sea, under a greyish cloud,
Thunderclouds taking shape, twenty leagues off
Mendocino Cape,
The crescent moon had rose, and amongst the twinkling
stars it froze.
And suddenly there came a whoosh, as the sea exploded
with a breach,
A whale, a sperm, a cachalot, from the sea did rise,
did blow and breach.
So close, so close, so very close,

Scarce within my reach.
It was a pleasant night in June, under a rather
melancholy moon.
Caught in its teeth, six metres of giant squid,
captured from beneath.
Leviathan and prey crashed back into the brine
in a frothy spray.
I watched with enraptured awe, my crew and I, not a word
could we say,

As this whale, this sperm, this cachalot, dove into the depths,
dark and grey.
With a splashing bow he was gone,
Concluding the grim ballet.

The sun's morning glow gave cry to the sky with a loud,
"There she does blow."
The whales, the sperms, the cachalots, all around us, they
did swim and breach.
Through the greyish gloom we saw the approach of the grisly
Goliaths of doom.
Nearer they came, these steel sheathed slayers of sweet
sentient grace,
We children of Ahab watched them approach with
fear upon our face.
Oh, how I despised them,
These loathsome slayers of grace.

We heard the thunderous shot; we saw the blood, as the
dying whale fought,
In the dark blue sea she thrashed in pain as bullets through
her body lashed.
Her hot breath shot forth in a pinkish mist from
this dying cachalot.

She arched her back in a twist and rolled in horrific pain,
To slaughter this wondrous armless Buddha was
senselessly insane.
And I could not help but wonder,
How many others had they slain?

Like a sad quixotic knight we raced our Zodiacs
with another pod in sight,
My small boat through the waves did rip as we
chased that evil ship.
The harpoon we blocked, as before that high foreboding bow
we rocked.
Before us the whales, the sperms, the cachalot
numbered a pod of eight,
Two young calves, five females with a large bull
as their protective mate.
A family waylaid by chance.
Could we avert their grisly fate?

In mortal fear, raced the whales, we followed with
the monster on our rear.
That steely prow did glide over the tide, cleaving the sea
like an axe.

The harpooner was grim, he aimed at my heart as
I looked back at him.
He could not kill a whale, a cachalot, withour
bodies in the way.
The Russian captain ran forward and to the harpooner
had his say:
His finger sliced across this throat,
As he screamed for us to stay away

Like a delicate shell my little boat rose upon a surging swell,
I was so near I could smell the fear in their vaporous breath.
I could see a spout misting the air, I heard the whalers shout.
I went surfing down into a trough when I heard that
horrific sound
The deadly missile whistled near overhead and I quickly
turned around.
And what I saw horrified me
As my heart began to pound

Like a woman tortured by a heartless fiend,I heard her
painful scream,
She rolled on the flood as a fountain of blood spurted
from her side.
"My God," I cried, watching helplessly, as in convulsions

she died.

Her hot blood spread like a malignant stain on the
surface of the sea,

The largest whale turned to the right, six others t
urned left to flee.

His tail rose and came down hard,

As his saddened fluke slapped the angry sea.

Beneath me the Leviathan swam towards the whaler
with the intent to ram,

The big gun was steady and they were ready, reloaded with
a merciless dart.

I saw his eye breach the surface, I saw the gun and knew
that he would die,

This whale, this sperm, this cachalot, face to face with a
monster on the sea.

In shock I sat in my tiny boat as witness to cold-blooded
murder on the sea.

In a fight most unfair he would die,

Slaughtered on that sullen sea.

At point-blank range the gun did spit, a roar shook the air, as
his body sank,

Slowly into the scarlet waters, he bellowed,

crazed with rage.
My tears did flow as the whalers smirked, and
shock vanquished all my fears.
This whale, this sperm, this cachalot, this savaged
lord of the deep abyss,
Slain by ignorant black hearted nameless men,
spineless and merciless -
Devoid of empathy, these killers on the sea,
Unmoved by the whales' distress.

In horrour I sat, until suddenly I caught the whale's
penetrating eye,
I looked at him and he looked at me and then he dove
beneath the sea.
Aghast, I saw a trail of bloody bubbles coming
towards me fast.
The whale, the sperm, this cachalot, rose from
the sea and towered by our side,
My first thought was that this great titan would slay me
before he died,
His teeth so close, his breath upon my face,
Steaming, streaming blood, cascading down his side.

Leviathan, his strength is great, and thus he has no

need to hate.

I saw in his eye that he understood, that we were there for his good,

Reflected in that great whale's eye, I saw myself, as crying for a reason why.

Slowly he sank into the dark depths, I watched him sink beneath the shroud,

Rain like tears upon me fell, beneath a towering thundercloud.

All was quiet on the sea,

As blood oozed up from that darkened shroud.

Amidst the violence and the strife, he had chosen to spare my life.

With relief and great emotion I sat in that boat upon that heaving ocean.

That eye, that eye, so beautiful and so real, oh my God it haunts me still;

Before he sank and departed, a message to me was imparted.

Repay this debt for your life, your course has now been newly charted.

You live to serve a greater good,

You must finish what you started.

That large orb, that sacred eye, like a sponge,
my soul it did absorb.
The whale, the sperm, the cachalot, had struck my heart with
one desire,
In its depths, I saw the past, felt the present, saw the
future in that living glass.
On that spot I quit the maddening insanity of
ruthless humanity.
I swore in a frustrated fit of angry profanity,
To forsake myself from
Mankind's festering inhumanity.

The dark and deep enchanted depths, does its
silent secrets keep.
Benthic vows unrecanted, weigh heavily on the
heart and mind,
The whale's hot blood still burns my soul and through
desire drives my will
The whales, the sperms, the cachalots guide my hand on
sea and land,
For in their service I am committed, and in their service
I do stand.
As the seas I have charted
Keep me sailing o'er the darkening sand.

Healing the Oceans

All sealife is under siege. The human population is skyrocketing; it's very evident an epic collision is set to occur. What can be done to ameliorate this ominous situation? Change is the only constant in life, and it's time to embrace the cofounder of the London School of Economics - George Bernard Shaw's dictum: "Progress is impossible without change, and those who cannot change their minds cannot change anything." To save the oceans we need commitment: "Real change can only come from legislation and the enforcement of the rule of law. We have the legislation and we have the laws, we just need to see politicians who care enough to insist on the enforcement of the laws," says Watson as Sea Shepherd has been doing the lion's share of protecting our seas, so far.

"The problem with our economic and political systems is that they focus on short-term and not long-term consequences of our actions. But all over the world there are people working to make the ecology movement what it is. And we have come a long way," says Watson. On all Sea Shepherd ships Watson flies the Five Iroquois Nations flag because, as he explains, their philosophy is the right ecological approach to protect nature and the human race: "Never do anything without thinking about the consequences it will have seven generations later."

In the 1960s off-coast of Leigh on the North Island of New Zealand, the rocky coastal reef was known as "Rock Barrens" because nothing grew there. Large sea urchins over-grazed the kelp forests, their predators Snapper and Pink Maomao were gone, overfished. The ecosystem had completely collapsed. In the early 1970s marine biologist Dr Bill Ballantine proposed a recovery plan for the kelp forest ecosystem. It was simple with brilliant results. In 1975, New Zealand created The Goat Island Marine Reserve, an area of six kilometres^2 (2.3 miles^2) making it a "no-take zone," any fisherman caught within the reserve faced a punitive fine of $30,000. Once the reserve was established Snapper and lobster returned and begun to prey upon over-populated sea urchins. The kelp forest ecosystem responded slowly at first and as the fish returned magnificent biodiversity followed. It took three years for the Snapper population within the reserve to become eight times greater than outside the "no-take zone." It took another two decades before the kelp forest ecosystems fully recovered from over-fishing. Today, there are fourteen times more fish species inside the reserve compared to outside. The biodiversity in the reserve is staggering: Buttery Perch, Silver Drummer, Porae, Red Moki, Leather Jacket, Blue Cod, Red Cod, Goat Fish, Hiwihiwi, Butter Fish, Marbled Fish, Red-Banded Perch and Demoiselles. Just off offshore there are lace corals, sponges, gorgonian fans, sea squirts and anemones. Deeper waters belong to the incredible luxuriant kelp forests providing habitat for myriad fish species, replete with those furtive inhabitants along the seabed, tucked into crevices or perched artfully under rock ledges like big Rock lobsters and sea urchins. Over the last thirty years, thousands of New Zealand school children have visited the Goat Island Marine Reserve, donned snorkels, fins and even scuba gear and experienced awe-inspiring marine biodiversity - ecological jewels within these lush kelp forests. The race to save the sea with tangible results from marine reserves has indeed begun.

Presently, New Zealand has 18 reserves providing necessary benchmarks for what occurs in undisturbed marine ecosystems. Without basic information only available from protected reserves "sustainable fisheries" is purely a myth. There are underwater-protected reserves in New England, St Lucia, Florida, California, the Bahamas and elsewhere all demonstrating the ocean's remarkable ability to regenerate its fish and other sealife populations. Australia recently created the largest fully protected marine reserve near two far-flung islands to help safeguard rare beaked and bottlenose whales, The Heard Island and McDonald Islands Marine Reserve now spans 71,200 kilometres^2 (27,490 miles^2) of Indian Ocean. Located 4,100 kilometres (2,548 miles) south-west of Perth; they are barren, uninhabited outposts considered among the most remote places on Earth, that will be safe from potential threats such as oil and gas drilling, as well as commercial fishing. It is definitely time for every country with marine coastlines to follow Australia's lead and increase marine protected reserves, substantially.

Watson agrees with me that nature is the most flawless system we know – so why not seek inspiration for solutions to modern problems and create products that are non-toxic? The first person to do this was the founder of modern science – an interpreter between nature and humans – Leonardo da Vinci, born in the middle of the 15th century. He drew all his inspirations from nature's blueprint, but it took 500 years before the applied engineering field of biomimetics was created. Millions of people around the world are working in small, medium and large companies in a rapidly expanding field called biomimicry; the design of human-made materials, devices and structures inspired by the architecture of living things. There are long-term jobs with an unlimited potential providing that humans protect nature rather than harm her. Biomimetics is offering college graduates life-long careers and fostering a deep appreciation for all life within all wild ecosystems, worldwide.

Already we've seen one example of Speedo mimicking sharkskin for its swimwear, but what else has the ocean offered humans by way of inspiration? This list not meant to be exhaustive, but rather to tantalise your curiosity and begin the illustrious process of stimulating your imagination. For remember this: "Humans are exceptional problems solvers and ingenious tool makers" – that's what we do best!

The structure of lobster's 13,000 mirrored tapered boxes within each of its eyes have inspired scientists to create a new X-ray vision space telescope called Lobster-ISS for use on board the International Space Station, facilitating exploration of our galaxy and beyond. The Venus Flower Basket is one of the world's rarest and most prised bits of flotsam. It is occasionally found washed-up along the beaches of Cebu Island, Philippines, where it resides at depths in excess of 5,000 metres (16,404 feet) in the western Pacific Ocean. Its hollow cylindrical glass-like skeleton measuring 300 millimetres (12 inches) long is comprised of fragile latticework similar to an intricate scaffolding system. The bone-white latticework acts as a protective refuge attracting tiny pairs of mating shrimp. As they grow so too does the Venus Flower Basket quickly entrapping the shrimp. Their offspring float with the brine through the latticework openings, but the parents remain contained, for life. Scientists from Lucent Technologies were intrigued with this elaborate latticework pattern within the Venus Flower Basket. Upon examination it revealed major fundamental construction strategies applicable to laminated structures, fibre reinforced composites, fibre optics (used in the world wide web) and diagonal reinforced square-grid cells.

Non-drip paint mimics the mucus of a snail, which is both a lubricant and glue. Epoxy glues mimics phenomenal glues from the bottom of barnacles and holdfasts of seaweeds and kelp forests. The shell of a snail is made up of a calcium carbonate, an otherwise brittle compound, yet it's robust because of its durable configuration. Present-day composite materials mimic this flawless detail. One biomimetic design used billions of times every day comes from Starfish ossicles or skeletons. The strength of the ossicle is derived from the molecular criss-cross formation of calcium carbonate compounds. This exceptional pattern has been applied to stiffen the fillers in all rubber tyres on cars and trucks, globally. Recently, researchers from Jacobs School of Engineering at University of California San Diego discovered that skeletons of seahorses can compress to less than half their size without any discernable damage to the design. Instead its approximately 36 square segments, each made of four bony plates loaded with collagen, glide past each other keeping the spine safe and re-assembling perfectly once the load is removed. The engineers are applying this configuration to create gripping devices for use in unmanned bomb detonations as well as tiny medical tools to work inside the human body. Another team of scientists from the Jacobs School has mimicked the flexible dermal armour of Leatherback sea turtles to develop state of the art bulletproof vests that provide soldiers more mobility and degrees of freedom compared to traditional rigid ballistic vests. The flexible dermal armour design acts as a high impact absorbent material, which protects against both bullets and shrapnel.

The Toronto-based company Whalepower was inspired by Humpback whale fins, in particular angular lumps of the pectoral fins that increase or decrease both lift and drag as the fin smoothly moves in either direction enabling sharp turns in the water. Applying this pattern to blades making energy, they created more stable, durable and quieter wind turbines, called "Tubercle Technology." The sinuous movement of fish inspired British scientists; they mimicked its body shape for a marine robot to monitor pollution in the sea. The wi-fi connected, life-like robotic fish is equipped with chemical sensors being used to locate sources of hazardous pollutants in the Mediterranean Sea and elsewhere. Ocean currents inspired the Australian firm BioPower System. They created an ocean power system that harnesses energy from the sea by mimicking the motion of underwater plants like kelp forests in their movements to generate electricity. Devices fixed to the ocean floor mimic the unparalleled shapes of tuna and sharks, aligning with the flow in the water in any direction, generating electricity with a reversed propulsion mechanism. Scottish-based Aquamarine Power has a wave-powered system inspired by oysters generating electricity using the motion of the waves to activate an oscillator to pump water through a turbine. It can operate in shallow shoreline waters making it a tremendous candidate for all marine-based countries to harness the sea's energy. Researchers from Fraunhofer Institute in Berlin, Germany, were inspired by sharkskin creating a new non-toxic paint formula for airplanes, boats and wind turbines reducing drag and increasing efficiency; it saves cargo ships up to 2,000 tonnes (2,205 tons) of fuel a year.

Bottlenose dolphins have inspired British scientists from the University of Southampton to create a new type of radar mechanism – a semiconductor tracker weighing two grams – to locate miners trapped underground or skiers buried in avalanches. The scientists were intrigued that dolphins could see fish with their radar beyond the vast clouds of bubbles they blow to herd their prey into smaller groups for feeding. Dolphins use echolocation sending out twin pulses varying in amplitude. The scientists created a device whereby both positive and negative pulses are sent out in twin pairs. Currently, human built sonar systems send out single radio pulses. The dolphin-inspired semiconductor device takes the pulse of a negative polarity and turns it into a positive polarity. The returning signal then comes back very strongly because adding a positive to a positive yields an even stronger detectable pulse. Even without this device the technology has a wide application, for instance; a person trapped in a collapsed building could be traced from their mobile phone even if it were switched off or the battery was dead. Or this technology can be applied to other forms of radiation like magnetic resonance imaging and light detection and ranging which, for example, scatters nonlinearly from combustion products, offering the possibility of early fire detection systems.

From sea urchins inspiring perpetually sharp tools to antibiotic medicines from seaweed to generating one terra watt of energy from the sea – enough to power 764 average coal-fired power plants or one third of the existing coal plants in operation – the oceans are truly an incomparable treasure chest: *Mare incognita*.

So how do we heal the oceans? The answer is simple, but not that easy. Watson believes we need to leave them alone, altogether "My position is that to save the ocean we need to save the fish and saving fish means not eating them. No one can call themselves a conservationist if they eat fish. As someone raised on seafood all I can say is that if I can give it up and adopt a vegetarian diet others can also." Based on all the scientific numbers I've thoroughly scrutinised, 80 per cent of the oceans require "no-take zones" enforced by stiff fines and long imprisonment sentences. But Watson cautioned me, "The problem with sanctuaries is that they are not enforced. We are fighting Japanese whalers in the Southern Ocean Whale Sanctuary. We are fighting shark finners in the Galapagos Marine Reserve. In practice there simply are no 'no-take' zones." It's not just dropping fish *per se* from your diet that will save the oceans it's chicken and meat too, says Watson "And eating meat also contributes to the destruction of the oceans. Forty per cent of all the fish caught in the sea is fed to domestic salmon, pigs, mink, foxes and chickens. We are even exploiting plankton as feedstock for livestock. It takes an average of 70 fish caught from the sea to raise one domestic salmon. Pigs now eat more fish than sharks and chickens now eat more fish than puffins and albatross." Currently, less than 1 per cent of the oceans are protected in marine reserves. That's entirely unacceptable. This much we do know, there is very little time left for Bluefin tuna, Leatherbacks, Loggerheads, sharks, rays, skates, seahorses, albatrosses and all commercial fisheries. Indecision is not an option. The fate of humankind is inescapably linked to the oceans, and they are dying, quickly. There is hope as US President Barack Obama formally established the expansion of the Pacific Remote Islands Marine National Monument in the central Pacific from around 225,000 kilometres^2 (86,873 miles^2) to nearly 2 million kilometres^2 (772,204 miles^2) or two times larger than the currently largest protected area, which is in Greenland.

At least 85 per cent of plastics in the oceans are from the land. Easy. Cut them off. I believe that globally by involving every primary and secondary school, based along all rivers, lakes, seas and oceans, we can engage these children and young adults with hands-on ocean conservation in-action projects; it's the surest way of instilling the laws of ecology and the Iroquois mantra that both Watson and I believe in, so strongly. Each year I involved my students in ocean plastic removal projects; they are thrilled and motivated knowing they are making a difference. It's a conservation ethic they carry with them for the rest of their lives. I also earnestly believe that each of us can make a difference by changing habits like becoming a vegetarian, reducing our consumption and reusing materials, and by volunteering to clean-up riverbanks, lakeshores, seashores and ocean beaches. As voters and consumers, we can exercise a unanimous and highly influential voice for the conservation of all marine life, worldwide. I encourage everyone to hand-write a letter and mail it to your elected officials, telling them to support more marine protected areas with a provision to heavily police them.

I asked Watson what is your most important message for the world? "The most important message is simply this: If the oceans die, we die! We cannot live on this planet with a dead ocean. Diminishment of biodiversity in the seas weakens the ecology of our oceans. We need diversity for interdependence and we need abundance to ensure diversity," says Watson as humans have entered the eleventh hour and its fifty-ninth minute.

Watson has but one wish for the oceans: "I would like to see an international oceans policy put in place. If such a policy existed, Sea Shepherd would not need to get involved. We already have all the laws and treaties we need to protect the oceans. The problem is the lack of political and economic will to enforce them. If that job was given to some international body or other, that would be a huge step towards protecting the ocean."

When I asked Watson what he wanted to be most remembered for? With a fond child-like grin he told me, "My poetry I hope." Although he's often seen wearing black his favourite colour is navy blue, his favourite recording artist is Lorena McKennitt and his favourite place to watch a sunrise or sunset "On the deck of a ship anywhere in the ocean really." He told me that his top three experiences on the sea were: "1) The hunting down in 1979 of the outlaw whaling ship *Sierra*, ramming it and later sinking it and ending its career forever. 2) Engaging the Soviet Union's Navy off the coast of Siberia in 1981 and not backing down to their guns and securing the evidence of their illegal whaling activities for the IWC. 3) In 1975, a dying Sperm whale, mortally struck by a Soviet harpoon could have killed me. He rose out of the water at an angle and would have fallen down upon me in my small inflatable boat but as his eye emerged from the sea, I saw understanding and I felt that the whale knew that we were there to protect whales and not to kill them. He pulled back and his head sank below the surface of the sea and he died. He could have killed me and made the decision to not do so. As a result I have felt indebted to that whale for my life for the last three and a half decades." The former USSR was a brutal whaling nation that exerted a disgusting sense of entitlement of the sea; based on good data now continuing to come to light – between 1948 and 1973 the Soviets exterminated over 180,000 whales that were never reported. Bureaucrats created a 25-year make work project; whales were murdered and wastefully discarded because they were so "easy" to kill.

Watson believes children are central to forthcoming healing process we are beginning to undergo: "What we need to do is not switch them off. Children are natural ecologists. Our educational system turns them into non-caring consumers and ecological sociopaths. They can teach us and if we listen to them they can." When I asked him if the children would ever forgive us for the ecocide? He paused then said, "I do not believe our children or their children will forgive us. We are stealing their heritage and laying it to waste, we are impoverishing their future and thus committing crimes against humanity."

The fate of Watson is unknown since skipping bail in Germany in July 2012 (while under arrest and pending a formal extradition request by Costa Rica) – he returned to the United States after spending 15 months at sea because Costa Rica and Japan had issued two Interpol Red Notices against him. Costa Rica alleged he violated navigational regulations dating back to charges stemming from a high-seas confrontation over shark finning in 2002. Japan has charged him with breaking into a vessel, damage to property, forcible obstruction of business, and injury related to a 2010 incident in the Indian Ocean. Costa Rica's Interpol Red Notice was dropped but they formally requested on November 5, 2013 that the US extradite him back to Costa Rica to face charges over the shark finning incident. Watson will challenge the Japanese notice in the US or France, where he is currently, if required. When asked about his destiny he closes his eyes remembering the words that his spirit guide spoke so many years ago in South Dakota, "I do what I must because it is the only thing I can do. It is the right thing to do, the just thing to do. I am a warrior for the Earth. I will live the life of a warrior and I will die a warrior's death."

Watson's poetry sings of this lifelong calling and mission to protect the whales and in doing so maintaining Earth's illustrious dance of life.

GRACE

By Captain Paul F. Watson

To save the life of one whale is to achieve grace.
To preserve the lives of one hundred whales is to achieve
grace a hundredfold.
To defend the lives of one thousand whales is to achieve
grace a thousandfold.

We are adrift on the vastness of the ocean,
It moves us.
The weather moves with us.
The currents move with us,
As we move with the weather and the currents.

We see with our heart, perceive with emotion,
We are the sea.
Our blood shares salt with the sea.
What we take, we return to the sea,
Our blood is pumped by the moon.

Grace mantles our bodies in whale lines,
Whale lines connect everything to everything in the sea,

And thus we see. Thus we hear. Thus we smell.
Thus we feel. Thus we know.

The dance moves north from the Southern Ocean,
The hearts we rescued continue to beat.
The flukes we saved continue to move through the waters,
The minds we preserved continue to dream.

The sea is cold but cradles the hottest of blood,
Whaling ships cradle the coldness of death.
The sea is a nursery,
The *Nisshin Maru* is a morgue.

We work in the nursery to preserve life,
Thus our souls are warmed and blessed,
The whalers work in the morgue to destroy life.
Thus their souls are withered and cold and graceless.

The whalers murdered 251 armless Buddha's
We saved 784 beautiful minds this year.
They murdered the present.
We unmurdered the future.

To save the life of one whale is to achieve grace.
To preserve the lives of one hundred whales is to achieve

grace a hundredfold.
To defend the lives of one thousand whales is to achieve grace a thousandfold.

I reckon we all owe Captain Paul Franklin Watson an enormous debt of gratitude for "Shepherding the Sea" – since 1982 he and his loyal band of volunteers have sailed the seven seas armed only with the United Nations World Charter for Nature, upholding international law protecting albatrosses, dolphins, seahorses, seals, sea turtles, sharks, tunas and whales from despicable poachers.

THE END

What Can You Do to Make a Difference?

Lots!

First things first. Once you have read this list, ask two people to ask two more people… and so on and so forth… to undertake some of the changes listed below. Together we can help reverse the tide, feel as though we are part of the solution and truly make a difference!

Support Sea Shepherd Australia, Netherlands, USA and Global

http://SeaShepherd.org.au

http://SeaShepherd.nl

http://http://SeaShpherd.org

http://www.SeaShepherdGlobal.org

Support The Vortex Project

http://www.parley.tv/TheVortexProject#Vortex1

Support Australia for Dolphins

http:// http://www.afd.org.au

Support Mission Blue

http://Mission-Blue.org

Support Blue Oceans Institute

http://BlueOcean.org

Support Ocean Alliance

http://www.OceanAlliance.org

Support Surfrider Foundation

http://www.Surfrider.org

Support.Oceana

http://Oceana.org

Support Heal the Bay

www.HealtheBay.org

Support International Fund for Animal Welfare

http://www.ifaw.org

Support All One Ocean

http://AllOneOcean.org

Support Ocean Preservation Society

http://www.opsociety.org

Support Blue Voice

http://www.BlueVoice.org

Support Think Beyond Plastic

http://PlasticPollutionCoalition.org

Support 5 Gyres Institute

http://5gyres.org

Support Earth Carers

http://www.EarthCarers.org.au

Lend a helping hand each

Ocean's Day (June 8) by cleaning

any beach or shoreline.

Lend a hand each Clean Up

Australia Day

(first Sunday in March) by helping

to prevent rubbish from entering our oceans.

http://CleanUp.org.au

Or start your own group and

regularly clean up beaches or river banks.

Please do not purchase any cosmetic products with squalene or exfoliators

containing polyethylene balls of micro-plastics.

Stop eating fish and seafood.

Don't eat Bluefin tuna, ever!

Become a vegan

//http://www.VeganSociety.com/

Don't ever buy tickets to dolphinariums.

Purchase 6 organic, bee-friendly cotton bags and only shop with them, refuse single-use disposable bags, instead buy plant-based bags and take them to the grocery store, re-use them again and again, and don't forget to launder them (cold water only) once a month.

Go organic, grow your own, plant a couple fruit trees in your yard and please no pesticides we need all the bees, every last one of them. And remember "You are what you eat!"

If you smoke, please be responsible; don't discard your cigarette butt on the beach nor on a city or town street-side.

Volunteer your time to any local marine conservation group.

Start a Facebook marine cause and share your conservation information.

Become more aware of ocean issues by subscribing to Google Alert.

Walk more, ride your bicycle or skateboard more, watch more sunrises and sunsets, walk barefoot in meadows, have more picnics, find your bliss and please drive less, way less!

Suggested Readings

Clover, Charles. *The End of the Line*, The New Press: New York, 2006.

Cousteau, Jacque Yves and Diole, Philippe. *The Whale, Mighty Monarch of the Sea*, Doubleday: New York, 1972.

Danson, Ted and D'orso, Michal. *Oceana: Our Endangered Oceans*, Rodale: New York, 2011.

Darby, Andrew. *Harpoon into the Heart of Whaling*, Da Capo Press: Cambridge, 2008.

Earle, Sylvia. *The World is Blue*, National Geographic: Washington D.C., 2009.

Earle, Sylvia. *Sea Change*, Fawcett Columbine: New York, 1995.

Ellis, Richard. *Tuna a Love Story*, Alfred Knopp: New York, 2008.

Essemali, Lamya and Watson, Paul. *Interview with a Pirate*, Firefly Books: Toronto, 2013.

Halter, Reese. *The Incomparable Honeybee*, Rocky Mountain Books: Victoria, 2011.

Halter, Reese. *The Insatiable Bark Beetle*, Rocky Mountain Books: Victoria, 2011.

Heller, Peter. *The Whale Warriors*, Free Press: New York, 2007.

Maser, Chris and Sedell, James. *From the Forest to the Sea*, St Lucia Press: Delray Beach, 1994.

Maser, Chris and Halter, Reese. *Life, The Wonder of it All*, Global Forest Society: Los Angeles, 2013.

Morikawa, Jun. *Whaling in Japan*, Columbia University Press: New York, 2009.

Morris, David. *Earth Warrior,* Fulcrum Publishing: Golden, 1995.

Mowatt, Farley. *Sea of Slaughter*, Key Porter: Toronto, 2003.

Parker, Steve. *The Encyclopedia of Sharks*, Firefly Books: Buffalo, 2008.

Safina, Carl. *Song for the Blue Ocean*, Henry Holt: New York, 1998.

Safina, Carl. *Eye of the Albatross*, Henry Holt: New York, 2002.

Safina, Carl. *Voyage of the Turtle*, Henry Holt: New York, 2007.

Watson, Paul. *Shepherds of the Sea,* The Sea Shepherd Conservation Society: Vancouver, 1980.

Watson, Paul. *Seal Wars*, Key Porter: Toronto, 2002.

Whitehead, Hal. *Voyage to the Whales,* Stoddart Publishing: Toronto, 1989.

Whitehead, Hal. *Sperm Whales Social Evolution in the Ocean*, University of Chicago Press: Chicago, 2003.

About the Author

Dr Reese Halter is an Earth doctor, an award-winning broadcaster, distinguished conservation biologist and Chair of Science at MUSE School CA. He enjoys organic gardening, building bee condos, racing sailboats, exploring beaches, moon watching and spending time in the high country with the ancient-ones: Great Basin bristlecone pines. Dr Reese and his Chessie live in Los Angeles, California.

For more information visit www.DrReese.com

Dr Reese Halter and Captain Paul Watson,
Sea Shepherd Conservation Society

Dr Reese Halter and Martin Sheen

Dr Reese Halter, Los Angeles

Dr Reese Halter and Sam Simon

Dr Reese Halter and Jeff Hanson,
Sea Shepherd Australia